ON THE TRAIL OF ADVENTURE

● **GERALD YOAKAM**
Professor of Education
University of Pittsburgh

● **M. MADILENE VEVERKA**
Director of Elementary Curriculum
Los Angeles Public Schools

● **LOUISE ABNEY**
Director of Speech Improvement
Kansas City Teachers College

LAIDLAW BROTHERS, INC., PUBLISHERS

Acknowledgments

For permission to use copyrighted materials grateful acknowledgment is made to the following authors and publishers:

American Book Company for "The Little Boy Who Loved Trees" from *Stories of Great Artists* by Olive Horne and Katherine Scobey.

D. Appleton Century Company for "Jack Jouett's Ride" by R. T. W. Duke Jr., from *St. Nicholas Magazine.*

Bobbs Merrill and Company for "The Search for the Beautiful" from *Why the Chimes Rang* by Raymond M. Alden.

E. P. Dutton and Company for "The Good Little Cranes Who Were Bad," from *Among the Pond People* by Clara D. Pierson.

Arthur Giddings for "A Sail with Captain Monson."

Harper and Brothers for "Trains" from *I-Go-A-Traveling* by James S. Tippett.

D. C. Heath and Company for "An Old Settler's Story" from *Stories of Pioneer Life* by Florence Bass.

Houghton Mifflin Company for "Daniel Boone in Trouble" from *Children's Classics in Dramatic Form* by Augusta Stevenson; for "The Sand-hill Crane" from *Children Sing in the Far West* by Mary Austin; and for two selections from *The Peterkin Papers* by Lucretia P. Hale.

Little, Brown and Company for "Eletelephony" from *Tirra Lirra: Rhymes Old and New* by Laura Richards.

The Macmillan Company for "A Boy in India" from *Totaram* by Irene Mott Bose.

G. P. Putnam's Sons for "Radiator Lions" from *Everything and Anything* by Dorothy Aldis.

Caroline Ridgway for "You'll Find Them in Australia."

Frederick A. Stokes Company for "Through a Shop Window" from *Come Christmas* by Eleanor Farjeon.

THE LAIDLAW BASIC READERS

Illustrations by Milo Winter, assisted by Billy Parks, John Merryweather, Walter Oschman, and Earle Kirkbride.

CHICAGO   NEW YORK   SAN FRANCISCO   DALLAS   ATLANTA

CONTENTS

Knowledge—People and Places

Beauty—Artists and Ideals

History—Indians and Heroes

Emotion—Sentiment and Fun

WAVE KLMMER

KNOWLEDGE
PEOPLE and PLACES

A Trip in a Trailer

PREPARATORY NOTE: Noisy trains on tracks high above the ground, corn so tall you need a ladder to reach its top, springs of boiling water, black bears at your doorstep begging for food, a road of salt—these and other interesting sights are in store for you as you read Dr. Yoakam's story of a trip which he and his family took. For the Dudley family whom you'll read about in the story are in real life the Yoakam family.

Going West

It was a fine bright morning. Father, Mother, Dick, and Barbara were up early. The Dudley family were ready to start from their home in Pennsylvania to take a long auto trip across the United States to California. The car and trailer were at the back door. Everything was packed, and they were all ready to go.

9

"We'll drive over to Grandfather Dudley's to say good-by," said Father.

Father and Mother rode in the front seat and Dick and Barbara got in the back with Jip, the dog. The children were excited to be really going. Soon they stopped at Grandfather's. Grandmother and Grandfather came out to say good-by.

"Have a good time for me," said Grandfather. "I'll look after everything on your farm."

"Have a good time," said Grandmother, "and give our love to all the family that you see." They waved to each other as they drove away.

At first they went slowly, but soon they began to go faster and faster.

"I can hardly feel the trailer behind," said Father.

"It looks like a big bug coming on behind. Let's call it 'The Big Bug,' " said Barbara.

"When will we get to Chicago and meet Uncle Tom and Aunt Eleanor and the children?" asked Dick.

"Tomorrow afternoon," said Father.

The country through which they were passing was rough. The road wound in and out among the hills, but "The Big Bug" followed right along. They passed through many small towns. At noon they stopped in a city and had lunch. Dick and Barbara thought it was great fun to eat in a cafeteria. Never before had they seen such long tables filled with so many good things to eat.

After lunch they saw fewer hills and their road passed many quiet farms. Father was interested in watching the farmers at work in their fields.

"I'll be so glad when night comes," said Barbara. "I want to sleep in 'The Big Bug.' Won't it be fun?"

"Yes, it will be like camping out," said Dick.

By six o'clock they were all getting tired and hungry.

"Don't you think we had better look for a place to stop soon?" asked Mother. "We must stop where we can buy milk," said she.

"And some steak," said Father. "My, but I'm hungry for some good steak!"

"So am I," said Barbara, who was always ready to eat steak with Father.

"Me too," said Dick, who forgot for the moment what his teacher had taught him about using the word "I."

After a while they saw a sign which read:

SHADY GROVE CAMP

2 MILES

TRAILER CAMP

In a few minutes they were in front of the camp.

"This looks good to me," said Father, as he turned off the road and stopped in front of the store.

"We would like to stop here for the night," said Father to the man who came out to the car.

"Our price is fifty cents," said the man.

Father handed the man a half dollar and asked, "Have you some good beefsteak in your store?"

"I surely have," replied the man, "the very best beef in the country."

When they had bought some steak, milk, bread and other things from the man, they turned into the

11

camp. Soon they were busy getting supper. Father lighted the little stove on one side of the room in the trailer. Mother started the cooking. Barbara set the table while Father and Dick began to make up the bed at the other end.

They had a fine supper. As they ate they could look out of the windows into the green grove. The sun had set and the evening was beautiful. But the family were tired from their day of traveling. So very soon they began to get ready for bed. The table and seats at the front of the trailer folded up and made another bed. They moved part of the side wall of the trailer and there was another bed for Dick. They pulled down a curtain and they had two rooms. "Isn't this great?" said Dick, when they were all in bed.

"Oh, I think it's just grand," said Barbara.

The next morning Dick and Barbara were awake early and saw the sun shining through the windows of their house on wheels. They dressed quickly and helped put away the beds so Mother could get breakfast. By seven o'clock they were on their way to Chicago. They drove through flat country all morning. By early afternoon they were in the suburbs of Chicago.

"Where are we going to stop in the city?" asked Barbara.

"It's all arranged," said Father. "We are on our way right now to the trailer camp where we are to meet Uncle Tom and his family."

After a time they came to a large park. They saw signs pointing to the trailer camp and followed

them until they found the place. There they found
Uncle Tom, Aunt Eleanor, Tommy, Ann, and Baby
Betty. The children greeted each other loudly and
were very happy to see each other. Uncle Tom had
a trailer much like Father's but a little larger. They
parked the trailers side by side and uncoupled them
from the cars.

"Let's all go sightseeing together," said Father. "What would you like to see first?"

"I should like to see Lake Michigan," said Barbara.

"How about the Loop and the skyscrapers?" asked Dick.

"I want to see the Field Museum," said Mother, smiling.

"Hold on there," said Uncle Tom. "Where shall we go first? One thing at a time."

"Well, I'll tell you," said Father. "We are on the south side of Chicago now. Let's drive down the Outer Drive which runs for miles right along the lake. Then we'll go west to Michigan Avenue and drive down it as we get near the big downtown business section. That way Barbara will see the lake, Dick will see the skyscrapers, and Mother can see the Field Museum as we pass it on the way. Tomorrow we can come back and go into the Field Museum."

So it was decided to take the drive that Father suggested. They all got into Uncle Tom's car, since it was the larger, and started out. Never before had Barbara and Dick seen such busy streets and boulevards. It seemed as if they were in a vast river of cars. There were cars behind them and cars in front of them. There were cars to the left six lanes deep. Everyone else seemed to be in a great hurry to get somewhere. Uncle Tom and his family were from New York City and so, of course, Uncle Tom didn't mind driving through heavy traffic.

As they drove along they could see many beautiful steam yachts and sailboats out on the lake. After a time they passed through the heart of the big downtown district with its towering skyscrapers and found themselves on Lake Shore Drive. They saw many beautiful mansions and the wonderful homes of very wealthy people, but the lake was the most interesting of all to Tommy and Dick.

By and by they turned around and started back. It was supper time when they arrived at camp.

The next day they went sightseeing again. They saw many strange and wonderful places. They visited the stockyards where more livestock are bought and sold than at any other place in the world. They drove through the busy Loop, which is the main business section, saw the elevated railroad, and went to the Field Museum and the Aquarium. Visiting the Aquarium was an exciting adventure for the children for they had never before seen so many strange fish.

The Father of Waters

Early the next morning the two families started again. All morning they traveled through flat country.

"I've never seen so many fields of corn before," said Dick, who was riding with the children in Uncle Tom's car.

"This," said Uncle Tom, "is the corn belt. We have seen corn all across Illinois, and we'll see it all across Iowa. Eastern Nebraska grows corn, too.

They say in this part of the country that corn is king."

"What does that mean?" asked Ann.

"It means," said Uncle Tom, "that it is the most important thing to the people here. When the corn crop is good and the price is right, the people have money. But if the corn crop is poor, or they cannot get enough money for it, the people are poor and have a hard time to buy what they need.

"Soon now, we are going to see the largest river in the United States. It is called the Father of Waters. Do any of you know what it is?"

"The Mississippi," cried the children.

Before them rose a high bridge. They saw a sign which warned them to go slowly as they rolled upon the bridge. Beneath them lay the big river.

"I thought it would be bigger," said Tommy.

"What makes it so brown? Why does it look so muddy?" asked Barbara.

"The Mississippi River runs through a rich farm country," said Uncle Tom. "It carries a heavy load of soil. It is the soil that makes the river brown. At its mouth the Mississippi has deposited so much soil that there is what is called a great delta many miles wide and long. All rivers of this kind carry soil to the sea."

"I should think," said Tommy, "that after a while they would take all the soil into the sea."

"That is just what many other people fear," said Uncle Tom. "Our government is trying to help save the soil so that it will not all run away in the rivers. Much good land will be saved in the future."

16

"See the big dam over there," said Dick. "Why do they have a dam here?"

"The dam keeps the water in the river from running away too fast," answered Uncle Tom. "In that way it helps save the soil and keeps moisture in the ground. The dam is also used to make electricity. In these low buildings at the end of the dam, the electricity is made which is used to run machinery and for electric lights."

They were across the river by this time and in the state of Iowa. When they stopped for lunch, the children were still talking about the Mississippi.

After lunch everyone wanted to be on the road again, for they were going to visit Uncle Henry's farm next. Uncle Henry was a brother of Father's and Uncle Tom's. They went almost a hundred miles. Then they turned off on a side road and soon reached Uncle Henry's farm. They drove up to a large white house in a grove of trees.

Uncle Henry and Aunt Margaret were waiting for them. They came hurrying out of the house and there was much laughing and shouting as they greeted one another.

Soon the women went into the house. The men and the children went with Uncle Henry to see the farm and the livestock. Dick and Barbara were surprised to see how large the farm was. It was much bigger than theirs. Uncle Henry said that he owned five hundred acres of land.

All the children were interested in the animals. They went out to the barn to see the pigs and the cows. Uncle Henry raised corn and fed it to his big herds of hogs. He also had sheep and horses.

"Father," said Dick, after they had visited the farmyard and gone into the buildings, "it seems to me that Uncle Henry has almost a whole town right here on his farm."

"It is almost like that," said Father. "This is a very large farm and it takes many people to run it."

Just then Tommy, Ann, and Barbara came along.

"We are going down to the duck pond to sail boats," said Tom. "Want to go?"

"Oh, yes!" shouted Dick.

With happy shrieks the children started off to the pond. When they got there they used sticks for boats and sent them sailing. They also had great fun watching some mother ducks and their little ones.

Jip and Rover, Uncle Henry's dog, chased squirrels in the woods. Dick and Tom ran after them. Ann and Barbara heard that Aunt Margaret was going to make ice cream and so they hurried back to the house to see if they could help.

Aunt Margaret was in the milk house. Here were many things which the children did not understand.

"What is that machine for?" said Barbara to Aunt Margaret.

"That," answered Aunt Margaret, "is a cream separator. It is run by electricity. And this is the electric ice-cream freezer. The milk is also kept cold by this electric refrigerator. Do you want to help me make ice cream?"

"Yes," said Ann. "It will be lots of fun. We always buy our ice cream at the store."

"All we have to do," said Aunt Margaret, "is mix up the milk, cream, eggs and sugar, add the flavoring, and turn on the current."

While the girls cracked the eggs and measured the sugar, she got out the electric mixer. Soon the eggs were beaten and the ice-cream mixture was ready to be put into the freezer.

There were so many interesting things for the girls to look at and examine that before they knew it, Aunt Margaret was calling, "Get your dishes, girls."

Just then Tom and Dick came in and wanted to know what was going on.

"Get some dishes," said Aunt Margaret, "and help yourselves."

That night at a big dinner of fried chicken and some more ice cream for dessert, Tom said, "I have found out why they call Iowa the state where the tall corn grows. We went into a cornfield after a rabbit and the corn was so high you would have needed a ladder to reach the top of it."

"Did you get the rabbit?" asked Ann.

"No," said Dick. "The rabbit went so fast that Jip and Rover came back with their tongues hanging out. Jip was puffing like an engine. And I guess he has never had so much fun."

"Neither have we," said Ann and Barbara together.

Several days after their visit to Uncle Henry's
farm, the two families were traveling along the high
plains of western Nebraska. On each side of the
road as far as they could see were flat plains and
rolling, low hills.

"Soon," said Father, "we shall be in North Platte.
It is an interesting town. Along here where we are
now the wagons used to go very slowly. Many
wagons were drawn by oxen. It took them many
days to make the distance that we now make in a
few hours."

By this time they had come to the town which
lay in the flat valley between two long rows of hills.

"Some people say," said Father, as both he and
Uncle Tom drove their cars into a filling station,
"that this is where the West begins."

"What does that mean?" asked Barbara.

"They mean that the country begins to be a grazing country instead of a farming country. Instead
of farming as we do in Pennsylvania and Uncle
Henry does in Iowa, out here they raise cattle and
sheep. The land is not rich like ours and they cannot raise such things as corn and oats very well. So
they plant a little corn in the valleys, raise hay and
grass, and herd cattle rather than raise hogs."

Father was interrupted by the station man who
came to wait on them. While Father had the car
filled with gas, Mother and the children went to a
store near by to buy the food they would need for their
next meal.

"What are we going to do next?" asked Dick when they were all back in the car and ready to go again.

"We are going to visit Yellowstone National Park," replied Father.

Yellowstone National Park

In the afternoon two days later the Dudley families, one behind the other, drew up at the south entrance to the park. Uncle Tom bought a guide book so that they would be sure to know where to find the most interesting places in the great park.

Yellowstone Park is the greatest of our national parks. It is in the northwest corner of Wyoming. Many thousands of people visit this great park every year to see the geysers, the lakes, and the mountains.

By the time the two Dudley families were settled at the trailer camp, it was supper time. After supper they talked about what they wanted to see while they were in Yellowstone Park.

"I want to see some bears," said Barbara. "They say they are very tame. Do you suppose we could see any tonight?"

"If we don't shut our doors tonight, you may have one licking your neck before morning," laughed Father.

"What is a geyser?" asked Dick.

"A geyser is a kind of hot spring. It throws up water and steam at intervals. Old Faithful is the name of the most famous geyser in Yellowstone. We'll all go to see it in the morning, but I think it's time for us to get some sleep now."

Soon the beds in the trailers were made, and everyone was ready for a long night's sleep. They did not sleep long, however, before they were wakened by a loud noise outside the windows of the trailers.

"Get up, children, and see your bears," whispered Father.

Dick and Barbara jumped out of bed and looked out the window. And there, sure enough, in the bright moonlight outside they could see two large black forms. The bears were looking for something to eat. By and by they went from sight into the dark forest.

"Those bears may be very friendly," said Barbara, "but just the same, I wouldn't want to meet one in the dark."

Dick and Barbara went back to bed and did not hear anything more until Mother called them in the morning.

For several days the Dudley families made trips in every direction. They did not know which was more wonderful, Old Faithful with its great plume of water and steam, or the great canyon where they watched the water falling and listened to its mighty roar. The bright color of the canyon walls, the geysers, the sparkling water, the forests, the inquisitive bears that wandered all over the park—all of these were very wonderful.

Salt Lake City

Early in the morning a few days after the Dudleys had visited Yellowstone Park they were nearing Salt Lake City. They were following a narrow, winding road between two hills. By and by the road suddenly opened up and they could see a city before them with bare, brown mountains behind it.

"There is Salt Lake City!" shouted Tommy and Dick together.

"It doesn't look very big," added Ann.

"Salt Lake City," said Father, "is not very large, as cities go. I think we shall want to do some sightseeing here. This city was founded by the Mormons. It is the greatest Mormon city. We want to be sure to see the Mormon temple."

"What is a temple?" asked the children.

"A temple is a church, only it is a very large and fine one," said Father.

Soon they were at the trailer camp where they uncoupled the trailers from the cars, and got ready to go sightseeing. They all got into Uncle Tom's big car and drove to the square where the temple is located. They learned that they could not go inside the temple, but they could visit the grounds and enter one of the other buildings.

After a while they decided that it would be fun to drive out to Great Salt Lake and go swimming. This queer lake is about twelve miles from Salt Lake City. It is a great lake but has no large streams running into it and none running out. Its water is very heavy with salt and that is why it is called Great Salt Lake.

Swimming in Great Salt Lake is not like swimming in a river or lake of fresh water as the Dudleys soon found out. The water has so much salt in it that the swimmer bobs up and down on the top like a cork.

Uncle Tom and Father tried lying down on their faces and then sat in the water as if in a chair. The children sat straight up and bobbed like corks. It was great fun.

The next morning they were up and away before the sun was very high in the sky. As they left the city they took the same road they had taken to visit the lake the day before.

"Today," said Father, "we shall go seventy miles straight across the great salt desert."

At first there was little sign of the white salt desert they expected to find. But the country got more and more like a desert as they went on. After a while they came to a place where the ground on both sides of the road was white like snow.

"Is that really salt?" exclaimed Dick.

Father stopped the car and he and Dick got out. Dick chipped off a piece of the salt with his knife.

"Sure enough," said Dick. "I guess nobody would be without salt for his potatoes here."

They went on and soon they came to a sign which told them they could drive out on the salt if they wanted to. Both Father and Uncle Tom turned their cars and went smoothly along on a salt road for a mile or two and then turned back to the paved highway.

Time for Fishing

One afternoon several days after the Dudley families had left Salt Lake City, they decided to take another side trip to do some more sightseeing. They had just entered Lovelace, Nevada, and were stopping to have lunch there.

"Tonight," said Uncle Tom, as they sat in a restaurant eating, "we are going to camp in what is known here as the land of the sky blue water."

"Where is it?" asked Barbara.

"It's high up in the mountains near Truckee, and it is said to be one of the most beautiful lakes in the world. I have always wanted to see it."

"What can we do up there?" asked Dick who liked to have something to do other than just stand around and look.

"Oh, there will be plenty to do," said Father. "I have read that it's a fine place to fish for big trout, and there are horses to ride, boats to row, and wonderful beaches."

26

"All right, that sounds good to me," said Dick. "Let's hurry and get there."

An hour later they left the main road and started for Lake Tahoe. After a while they began a gradual climb on a winding road in a forest of pines and redwoods. As they climbed, the road became more winding and steeper. At last they reached a high point where they could look down on the lake below.

The bright sun shone on the lake. The water of the lake was a bright sky blue except along the edges. There it was shallower and a rich dark green. Off in the distance they could see high mountains with snow-capped peaks. Dark pine trees covered the lower slopes of the mountains. "Oh, Father!" exclaimed Barbara, "I think this is the most beautiful place I have ever seen."

"I'd like to stay here forever," said Dick in a quiet voice.

"I've been told," said Father, "that there is a very fine camp around the end of the lake. We shall stop there tonight."

In a little while they came to a great camp among the pine trees. There was a hotel, a store, many cottages, and tent houses among the tall trees. In a fenced yard near the hotel were some white-tail deer. The deer were so tame that they came to the fence looking for food. The children enjoyed watching them.

"Come on, boys," cried Uncle Tom. "Let's try our luck at some fishing."

Uncle Tom arranged with a fisherman to take them out in a boat to fish for trout. The fisherman

27

explained that they would have to use a long line made of copper and use a large minnow as bait. Soon they drove to the place where the fisherman said they were likely to catch the best fish.

"Let the line down until you can feel the bottom," advised the fisherman. "Then pull the line up a way and let it down again. Keep doing that."

Uncle Tom did as the fisherman instructed while the boys watched every move.

"Is it very deep here?" asked Tom.

"About eighty feet," answered the fisherman. "Of course, it is much deeper out there in the middle. This is a very deep lake. That is why the water is so blue."

Just then Uncle Tom felt a great pull on his line. Slowly and steadily he began to pull in the line, hand over hand.

"Keep your line steady," said the fisherman. "Bring him up beside the boat and I'll net him."

But Uncle Tom did not find that very easy to do. The fish wasn't ready to be brought up. Uncle Tom hung on as the fish dashed first this way and that. But after a while the fish became tired and Uncle Tom got him nearer and nearer to the boat. The fisherman leaned over the side with the net ready.

"I see him," he said, "and he's a big one! Bring him alongside now and don't let your line slip."

"I won't. I wo-o-o-n't!" said Uncle Tom. "Here he comes!"

The fisherman leaned over and slipped the net under the big fish. He lifted it into the boat; it thrashed furiously in the net. Then the fisherman

took a heavy stick and hit the fish sharply on the head. It lay still on the bottom of the boat.

"He should weigh about sixteen pounds," said the fisherman.

"Whew-ee!" said Tommy. "What a fish!"

"That was worth all the trip out here," said Uncle Tom.

Father and the rest were waiting on the dock for the fishing party.

"Did you get any fish?" called Father.

"One trout," answered Uncle Tom.

"One!" they all cried, looking disappointed.

Just then they came alongside the dock, where Father could see the big fish.

"Oh!" they all cried at once, while Father began to take out his big hunting knife.

"Well, well, I see!" said Father. "One little trout for supper, but he's big enough so we can cut out a lot of steaks from his sides. Hurry up. I'm hungry."

It was several days later. The Dudleys were on the main highway which would soon lead them over the Sierra Nevada Mountains and into the big valley of California.

"Today," said Father, "we shall cross the highest pass we have met. It is called Tioga Pass."

They rolled along a smooth highway which gradually became steeper. Soon they were winding around hairpin turns and climbing steep grades.

"Well," said Father, "I've always wondered whether we could haul this trailer over high mountains and I guess I'm going to find out."

Just then they began to ascend a still steeper grade. Father changed the car to second gear. The radiator began to spout steam.

"I guess," said Father, "that we'll have to let her cool off." He signalled to Uncle Tom that he was going to stop. There was a wide place in the road and Father turned into it. Uncle Tom did not stop but called as he went by, "Come on. We're almost up."

Father started again. Soon they saw a sign which read, "Summit, 8900 feet." When they started down they wound down a mountain road for an hour.

"Today," Father said, "we shall enter the great valley of California. First we shall pass through a fruit belt. We shall see orchards of peaches, pears, plums, and apples."

On and on they went for several days. Mother was getting anxious to see her father and mother who lived in a little town near Los Angeles. At last they were humming along the broad highway within a few miles of the little town where Grandma and Grandpa Howell lived. Uncle Tom and his family had left the travel party to visit other friends in Los Angeles.

"I can hardly wait until we get there," said Barbara. "I want to pick oranges from Grandma's tree."

"And I," said Father, "want to see Grandpa's walnut, apricot, and orange groves. It must be very interesting to see how they farm out in this country. Did you ever see such neat groves of trees?"

"It looks," observed Dick, "as if they farmed trees out here just as we farm our cornfield at home."

They were passing through a section in which walnut and apricot trees seemed to grow everywhere. Here and there among the trees they saw what appeared to be white tiles placed at regular distances from each other.

"I wonder," said Dick, "what those white things are."

"Those are water outlets," said Father. "This country is so dry that they have to water the trees by irrigation. They plow ditches between the rows of trees and then let the water flow through the ditches."

"Where do they get the water if the country is so dry?" asked Barbara.

"Some of the water is pumped from under the ground, and some they get from the water reservoirs where water is stored from the mountains."

"This is the town where they live, isn't it?" asked Mother excitedly.

"Yes, we're nearly at the end of our journey," said Father.

In a very few minutes they came to the house where Grandma and Grandpa Howell lived. Father stopped the car and Mother jumped out first. She took both Grandpa and Grandma in her arms at once. Grandma cried a little, she was so happy to see them. And soon Grandpa had Dick and Barbara by the hands leading them up to the house.

32

"We are all ready for you," said Grandma. "Lunch is all ready and we have lots of good things to eat, including orange marmalade and hot biscuits. Are you hungry?"

"Are we?" said Dick and Barbara in the same breath. "And how we love orange marmalade and hot biscuits," said Dick.

Soon they were all gathered around a long table on Grandpa's porch which overlooked the rose garden. Such chattering as there was! Everybody wanted to talk at once.

"We have been expecting you for a week," said Grandma. "Every day Grandpa has walked up and down on the front walk and looked down the road. He has been so excited."

"Yes," said Grandpa, "and Grandma has been making biscuits every day."

They all laughed and Grandma wiped her eyes a little and smiled happier than ever.

"Now," said Father, "I have a great surprise for you, including Mother." Grandma and Grandpa looked wise and very happy for they knew what he was going to say.

"What is it?" asked Mother, Barbara, and Dick all at once.

"We are going to stay all winter in southern California. Grandma and Grandpa have decided that we just have to stay to keep them company this winter. And it will be a lot of fun to escape a cold winter for once, don't you think?"

"Oh, won't it be wonderful?" they all cried.

"What about school?" asked Dick.

"Oh, I guess they have a school in this town," laughed Father.

Everyone was excited and happy. It was a very pleasant ending to a wonderful journey.

—*Gerald Yoakam.*

To Improve Your Reading

If you want to become a better reader, you will work like a football player. But instead of throwing passes and running through center, you will practice reading skills. You have two coaches—your teacher and the authors of this reader. Together they will help you learn what the skills are, and how to master them. Here are the main skills, or abilities, you should develop and practice this year.

1. Ability to understand and remember the main thought in whatever you read.
2. Ability to remember the most important details in what you read.
3. Ability to find information.
4. Ability to organize information.
5. Ability to use words well, and know many of them.
6. Ability to think for yourself.
7. Ability to speak well.
8. Ability to say in your own words what you read or hear others say.
9. Ability to appreciate beauty of different kinds.
10. Ability to use your own experience to help you understand what you read.

There are more skills, of course. But if you really understand and use these, you will get along very well. Every one of the exercises and suggested activities will help you learn one or more reading skills.

Test and Study Exercises

1. Why is this story in the part of your book called "People and Places"?

2. Name three things the Dudleys saw in Chicago.

3. Write in your own words the meaning, or definition, of each of these words: cafeteria, skyscrapers, boulevard, groves, irrigation.

4. Be able to express in your own words what each of these sentences says:

> The next morning Dick and Barbara were awake early and saw the sun shining through the window of their house on wheels.

> Soon they were at the trailer camp where they uncoupled the trailers from the cars, and got ready to go sightseeing.

Suggested Activities

1. Tell where you can find out more facts about the "Father of Waters."

2. Tell in what ways the children were helpful on the trip.

3. Make a list of eight or ten facts you have learned in this story. Number your facts in the order of their appearance in the story.

On the Mississippi

PREPARATORY NOTE: Perhaps you have seen boats on a great river at night and listened to the sounds they made and to the sounds of the wind and the water. The author of this poem has, and in the poem she describes those sights and sounds. The poem is arranged so that the class may read it aloud together. As you read the part assigned to you, be sure that you speak clearly and that you pronounce every word correctly. Try also to make the tone of your voice and the speed of your reading suit the sounds and sights described in the poem.

All: Hoo-hoo-hoo-oo . . .
      Hoo-hoo-hoo-oo . . .

Solo: A whistle in the night!
      A steamboat, decked with lights like stars,
      Is coming into sight.

All: Swish-sh-sh . . . swish-sh-sh . . .
      Swish-sh-sh . . .

Solo: Hear the restless waves
      Breaking, as the boat moves on,
      Against the rocky caves.

All: Putt-putt-putt . . .
      Putt-putt-putt . . .

Solo: A tug-boat sputters by—
      Energetic, businesslike,
      Beneath a starry sky.

All: Whew-ew-ew . . . whew-ew-ew . . .
Whew-ew-ew . . .

Solo: The night wind in the trees
Is whispering a ghostlike tune
Echoed by the breeze.

All: Moving—ever moving—
The river flows along;
Wheels and whistles, winds and waves
Sing the river's song.

—Louise Abney.

Test and Study Exercises

1. Copy all the lines in the poem that tell of things the poet wants you to hear.

2. Choose any three or four line part of the poem and express in your own words what the poet says.

Suggested Activity

Have you ever been on the Mississippi, or any other great river? If so, be ready to tell the class about that experience.

A Sail with Captain Monson

PREPARATORY NOTE: Bob Jones is an American boy very much like you or the boy who sits next to you at school. Bob thought that it was a great adventure to sail the English Channel with Captain Monson. Read the story to see whether you agree with him.

Crossing the English Channel

A few summers ago, Bob and his Uncle Bill went to Europe. They had spent their first few days in Paris, and had not thought of leaving it soon. But as they stood one day on the busiest corner in the city Uncle Bill rose up on his toes and yelled, "Hey, Ed Monson!" And from then on things happened.

From somewhere out of the moving crowd of people and traffic a big man with a red face and a fine smile came shoving his way through to Uncle Bill and Bob. As people swirled around them the two men shook hands, and Uncle Bill introduced Bob.

"Captain Monson, my nephew Bob Jones," said Uncle Bill. Bob felt his fingers swallowed by the captain's immense hand, and felt the big man's other hand smack him on the back.

"Glad to see you, glad to see you," the captain's voice boomed out. "Well met, friends, well met." The captain seemed to enjoy saying everything twice. "I'm just off for a trip, just off. You both must come. Yes, sir. Where's your stuff? Grab it and come along." Already the captain was taking them along the street. "No trunks, you know, no trunks. I've got a small boat this time. Leave the French coast in two days. Got to finish buying supplies now." The captain was striding away from them. "I'll meet you at the city pier in Le Havre at ten Wednesday morning. So long!" and the captain was gone.

"Well," said Uncle Bill, "how do you like my friend the sea breeze, Bob?"

"Can we go with him?" That's all Bob wanted to know.

"Can we go? Why, boy, we've got our orders. Of course we'll go."

That was the good thing about traveling with Uncle Bill. He never had plans to bother about. He took the best thing that came up, and liked it.

They were in the French port of Le Havre on Wednesday morning. "The captain didn't tell me the name of his boat," said Uncle Bill, "but if he's in town we'll hear him."

And hear him they did, as soon as they got out of their car at the pier. The captain was shouting in English at a Frenchman who could not understand. But as soon as he saw Uncle Bill and Bob he turned his shouts to them, and the Frenchman slipped away.

"Just giving that Frenchman an English lesson," cried the captain. "Funny how these foreigners can't understand our language." Then the captain laughed. That was one of his little jokes—pretending that the French were the foreigners, and not he.

"Well, mates, we're off in a half hour. There's my ship over there—the Wave Skimmer. We'll get aboard soon and get out of this country. We'll cross the channel. I'm going over to England and see the king. Yes, sir, see the king. Don't look important, boy. Anybody can see the king—especially if you have good field glasses, which I have. The king will be at the yacht races, at Cowes, near the Isle of Wight."

"Are you going to race?" Bob asked.

"Race, in that old tub? Why, boy, she can't race. Can't race at all. She's a schooner, fast of her kind, but not a fast kind. No sir, no races for us. No races at all. We'll be lucky to get across the channel. Very lucky. But come on, come on now. We'll push off. Ahoy there, give us a boat!" The captain's voice shot out over the harbor like a cannon roar, and two men climbed down the side of the Wave Skimmer and jumped into a small boat, which the captain called a dinghy.

"Now, Bill," said the captain, acting serious for the first time. "You sure you want to come with me? Sure? I have no engines—not an engine. All sail, you know. If there's no wind, we stay where we are, where we are. The crew has no experience. None at all, you know. Been on a boat before, but never pulled the ropes. They think it's fun. Fun, you know, well?"

"So do I!" said Bob.

"You can't scare us away, Ed."

Soon they were climbing up the rope ladder, and Captain Monson gave the order to cast off. The sails were set, a stiff breeze was blowing, and the Wave Skimmer set off for the open channel.

Captain Monson left Uncle Bill and Bob to themselves while he gave orders and steered the ship calmly through the crowded harbor waters. Not until they were well away from all the other ships in the harbor did he turn the wheel over to another man and join them.

"Now then, down this way. I'll show you your bunks. Here's the mate's cabin. Yes, sir, the mate's cabin, but I have no mate. So dig in there. Mine's over there. Here's my room and bath. Ha! ha! The only baths you'll get are buckets of salt water tossed over you on deck. No luxuries on this ship. No luxuries. Good food and a soft bunk. That's as far as we go, far as we go. Well, make yourselves cozy, mates. I'll be off. Only two rules for passengers on this ship—don't get in the way, and don't get off the boat till we touch land. I don't want to have to stop and pick you out of the sea."

Uncle Bill sat down on the edge of his bunk. "I always get tired when I'm with that man," he said. "He's a regular whirlwind."

"Is he a real sea captain?" Bob asked.

"No, he just loves sailing. He used to be a banker in New York. He made a lot of money and decided to spend the rest of his life having fun. He has no family, but he has friends all over the world. Let's go up on deck."

The Wave Skimmer was going at a great rate. All sails were set. Behind the boat was a white streak of bubbles and way off to the right a big freight boat ploughed awkwardly through the waves. Soon they saw to their left a graceful liner slipping along.

42

"Wouldn't give a cent for all the steamers in the world," said the captain, leaning on the rail with Bob and Uncle Bill. "Give me sails, every time. Yes sir, every time."

The winds continued. Their trip across the channel was swift and thrilling to Bob. He never grew tired of watching the prow of Wave Skimmer crack down on the great waves and ride through them as though they were nothing. That night he listened to the stories Captain Ed told of strange ports and waters of the world. And then in the morning they saw land.

Off the Coast of England

"That's Portsmouth off there," the captain said a little later. "Yes, sir, Portsmouth. The Isle of Wight's off there. We're right smack to the south of England. We'll slip in to Cowes and see what's going on."

The boats around Cowes were not like the liners and working craft they had seen in the harbor at Le Havre. Here they were all trim vessels, steam yachts bright with white paint and polished brass, and sailing yachts built for racing.

"There's one thing I always do in Cowes," said the captain one morning. "I like to make the English mad. They're funny people in some ways. Look over there. See that building? That's the club house of the Royal Yacht Squadron. Said to be one of the most exclusive clubs in the world. You know a thing's exclusive when they won't let anyone else in

43

unless they think he's perfect or has something they want. Yes, sir, that's exclusive.

"Let me tell you. Ever drink tea? Then you've heard the name of Lipton, maybe. Well, sir, there's not a more famous sailorman in the world than Sir Thomas Lipton. He's also one of the richest men in the world. But the English are sometimes funny people. Yes, sir, funny people. Old Sir Thomas once kept a store. He was what the English call 'in trade.' And they won't have him in their Royal Yacht Club because he once kept a store. Heigho! Do you know what I do? I march right up to the club buildings every time I'm here and I ask the steward of the club most politely, 'Does Sir Thomas Lipton happen to be in?'

"And the steward freezes. Yes, sir, he freezes right up. And he says, 'No, sir, we have no such person. Sir Thomas Lipton? No, sir, sorry sir, but he doesn't belong.'

"And then I laugh—a regular horse laugh I give him. Regular horse laugh. And then he shows me out. Sir Thomas doesn't belong. Ha! ha! ha! Can you imagine that? Then I'll bet this steward dashes off for a 'spot of tea,' as the English say, and it'll be Lipton's tea, no doubt. Heigho! So it goes, yes, sir, so it goes."

"Look!" said Bob, some time later, "those yachts are moving. Are they going to race?"

"Sure enough," Captain Monson said. "They'll be lining up now. We're out of the way. They'll go way around us. Yes, sir, way around us. We'll get a look at the king now. There's his ship over there,

the one with the fancy flag. He'll go trailing along pretty much as he pleases. The king has to have some rights, and that's about all that's left him. Yes, sir, the King of England is a nice man, but he has no power. Take a look, Bob."

Bob looked through the field glasses and saw the gay party on board the king's yacht.

"I see him," cried Bob. "He's not very big, is he?"

Bob was disappointed.

"The boy thinks a king should be seven feet tall," said the captain. "But they're human beings like us. They just have better uniforms. Yes, sir, better uniforms and more of them. Look! there they come —the racing boats!"

Everyone looked out over the bay as the beautiful yachts came flying around a buoy which marked a point in the course. The captain knew all the yachts and owners, and cheered for each boat as it passed. He didn't seem to care who won. In fact he didn't want to stay in Cowes any longer.

"We'll be off. Up anchor!" he shouted. Then followed more orders and with sails set the Wave Skimmer slipped through the harbor and out around the Isle of Wight into the sea again.

"We're off for Falmouth," said the captain. "We've had enough of this."

"It must be wonderful," said Bob, "to be able to do what you want, and never ask anyone."

"Well, it is, my boy. It is. But I've made my own way. I got along with others. I worked for others. I went through all that. Now it's my turn. Heigho! It's a great life."

For a moment the captain just smiled in pleasure, then he cried out to his sailors, busy at the ropes and the wheel and on the deck, "Strike up a tune, lads, just for the fun of it."

And he began in his big voice to sing a song of the sea. All the men took it up and soon the jolly song sounded from everywhere on the boat. Bob and Uncle Bill joined in, and as they sailed along the coast of England, Bob thought he had never had a happier time in his life.

"Off there," yelled the captain, "is Plymouth, where the old pilgrims took ship for America. Oh, lots of things started in England. Heigho! But America's the land for us. Yes, sir, the land for us. *America*, boys, swing into it!"

The old ship seemed ready to burst with sound as all joined in the song of their country.

As they finished, the captain looked to the shore. "Lads," he said, "take a look at old England. There she lies. And keep this in mind, lads. Keep this in

46

mind. Here we are on her coast. Yes, sir, right here. But in another way, lads, in another way, we've come a long way from old England. Heigho! The world's a great place, but we know the best place."

And so they sailed on, with song and happy shouts, along the coast to Falmouth, in the southwest corner of England. They anchored in the harbor beside the *Cutty Sark*, famous all over the world as one of the finest ships that ever fled before the wind.

"And now," the captain said, "we're through for this trip, and I'm off for London by rail. The Wave Skimmer will lay up here till I come back."

With a big kind laugh and a handshake Captain Monson said good-by to his guests and was rowed to shore.

"We'll go soon too, Bob, only we'll take a look at this part of the country before we go up to London. Over that way is Cornwall, an interesting part of England."

"Everything's interesting," said Bob. "Heigho! as the captain says, let's go!"

—*Arthur Giddings.*

Test and Study Exercises

1. (a) In what city did Bob and his uncle meet Captain Monson? (b) From what French city did the Wave Skimmer sail?

2. Where were the yacht races?

3. What kind of boat was the Wave Skimmer?

4. Copy on your paper the sentences that are true. There are four of them.

Bob and Uncle Bill met Captain Monson in China.

The captain had the habit of repeating his words.

They sailed from the French port of Calais.

The ladder on Wave Skimmer was made of rope.

The first English port they saw was Portsmouth.

Cowes is in the Isle of Wight.

Wave Skimmer won the race.

5. Look up and write the meanings, or definition, of these words from the story: pier, striding, foreigners, exclusive, steward, buoy, swirled, luxuries.

Suggested Activity

Find, on a map of Europe, the cities and other places mentioned in the story. Copy the outline of the map, write in the places, and connect them with lines to show the route of Wave Skimmer.

Trains

PREPARATORY NOTE: As you read this poem, try to picture in your mind everything which it mentions.

Over the mountains,
Over the plains,
Over the rivers,
Here come the trains.

Carrying passengers,
Carrying mail,
Bringing their precious loads
In without fail.

Thousands of freight cars
All rushing on
Through day and darkness
Through dusk and dawn.

Over the mountains,
Over the plains,
Over the rivers,
Here come the trains.

—*James S. Tippett.*

Test and Study Exercises

1. Write three or four sentences that tell in your own words all the ideas or word pictures the poet expresses in "Trains." If you would like to, write your own little poem about trains.

2. Perhaps your teacher will ask the class to read the poem aloud together. She may ask you to read certain lines, or a stanza. When you are given certain parts to read aloud, be sure that you know exactly how to say every word clearly and with the right expression.

Word Travelers

PREPARATORY NOTE: Words, like people, travel from country to country. Sometimes they are changed during their journey; sometimes they remain the same. Have you ever used a word which came from some other country?

Families coming to America from foreign lands brought with them not only their household goods and native customs, but many of their favorite words as well. A number of these words were so interesting and useful that their neighbors borrowed them and used them. In that way people from other countries helped us build our language. You will become better acquainted with a few of these word travelers from lands across the sea.

From France

All of you, at one time or another, have ridden in an *automobile*. The cars themselves are American-made; but the word *automobile* came to us from France. The French made it up from two words taken from older languages. From the Greek they took *auto*, meaning *self*, and from the Latin *mobile*, a word that means *moving*. They called the first cars automobiles because in contrast to the horse-drawn carriages and wagons, they appeared to be *self-moving*.

Sometimes automobiles are driven by *chauffeurs*. That word came from France, also. It is pronounced sho-fur. In France it used to mean *one who carries a stove*. But today, both there and here, it means a skilled driver. *Garage*, where the automobile is kept, is another word traveler from France.

Have you ever eaten in a *café*? This word came from both France and Italy. The word *café* means coffee; and even today if you were to say *café* to a waiter in France, he would serve you a cup of coffee. In our country, however, the word *café* means a place where not only coffee is served, but meals as well.

The word *restaurant* came to us from France by way of England. The Old French word meant *to restore;* the present meaning is a *public eating place.* We can see from this that the old meaning is still true, because all of us have felt our energy restored after eating a meal in a restaurant.

Whenever you see the capital letter F after a word in your dictionary [F.] you may know that you are meeting a word traveler from France. The letters [O.F.] will tell you that the word is even older and came to us from the Old French.

From Spain

Cafeteria is a Spanish word traveler. In Spain the word meant "coffee shop." In the United States a *cafeteria* is a kind of restaurant in which, as you probably know, many prepared foods—meats, vegetables, salads, desserts, breads, and drinks—are displayed upon a counter. As you pass by you make selections of your favorite foods, place them upon a tray, and carry them to a table for eating. Perhaps you have done this very thing.

Have you ever tasted *chile con carne*? This is a Mexican food but it has a Spanish name. It is very hot and very peppery, as the name indicates. *Chile*, in Spanish, means *red pepper; con* means *with;* and *carne* means *meat. Chile con carne*, therefore, is a dish made of minced red peppers and meat, with chile beans usually added.

Another food sometimes served with *chile con carne* is the *tamale.* Here, again, we have a word traveler from Spain describing a Mexican dish which has become popular in our country. *Tamales* are made of corn meal and ground meat. They are flavored with red pepper and served hot, usually wrapped in a corn husk and tied with a small string.

Whenever you see the letters Sp [Sp.] after a word in your dictionary you will know that it has come into our American language from Spain.

From Germany

Delicatessen is a word imported from Germany. Words, you see, as well as goods and food stuffs, are imported. *Delicatessen* means already prepared foods, such as cooked meats, salads, relishes, sausages, cheeses, and preserves. The word for us, however, usually means the store where such interesting and tasty foods may be bought.

Kindergarten is another word traveler from Germany. *Kinder* is the German word for *children; garten* in German means *garden.* Therefore, a *kindergarten* is really a *children's garden* where they meet together to learn new games and do other interesting things. As you know, young children in America today begin their school life in the *kindergarten*, just as some of you did several years ago.

Have you ever seen a *dachshund*, the dog with the very short legs in comparison with its length? This small hound comes from a breed originating in Germany. It was used in hunting to track badgers and foxes. The word itself comes from two German words: *dachs*, meaning *badger*, and *hund*, meaning *dog*. So in *dachshund* you have two words in one—badger-dog in our language.

When you find a word in your dictionary followed by a capital G [G.], you will know that it is a word traveler from Germany.

From Italy

Many of our musical terms have come from Italy. This is not surprising, because many of our great singers were born in that country. Even the laborers along the Mediterranean Sea have been called "singing sons of Italy." Italian words sing, too. Here are a few of them which are frequently met here in America.

The word *adagio* means *a slow movement*. It also means *in an easy, graceful manner*. It applies to music and to dancing. In Italian, the *a* has a very soft sound, very much like *ah;* and the word is called à-dä'-jo. Try it. Even the pronunciation of the word is musical.

Allegro and *allegretto* also came from Italy. Can you find these words in your music books at school or on the sheets of music in your home? *Allegro* means *brisk, lively, a fast movement. Allegretto* means quick, also; but not so lively as *allegro*. Don't the words themselves seem to dance for you? Check the pronunciation of these words in the dictionary and see how musical they sound as you say them. In Italian, long *e* is often pronounced like long *a*.

Cantata comes from the Italian word which means *to sing*. Choruses, solos, and other forms of music arranged in a choral composition are called a *cantata*. Have you ever heard a cantata sung at church or on the radio?

Finale, as you might guess, means the *ending*. It also is a word traveler from Italy. So are *intermezzo*, *libretto*, *maestro*, *moderato*, *piano*, *pianissimo*, *tempo*, *viola*, and *violin*. How many of these words do you know? Some of the meanings you could almost guess, but you can make sure by looking in your dictionaries.

Whenever you see It [It.] after a word, that word came from Italy; but it is yours when you make your own use of it.

From ancient Rome, the word *pencil* has come to us. There it was called *pencillus*, which meant *a little tail*. Artists and writers used this *little tail* or *brush of hair or bristles* for writing. That is how it gained its present meaning. Today, in China and Japan, a very fine brush is still used for writing.

Pen also came to us from ancient Rome. The Latin word *penna* meant *feather*. The first pens were feathers or quills, and while we no longer use them for practical purposes, the name remains to remind us of the old manner of writing, years ago.

—*Louise Abney.*

Test and Study Exercises

If your teacher wishes, you may play this word game. The teacher will divide the class into several groups.

Each group will represent a country, as Italy, France, Germany, Spain. Then each group will be given time to select from the dictionary word travelers from the country it represents.

One group then decides which of its word travelers it will present for the other groups to guess. You may act out the word, define it, or describe it.

As hints you might tell the number of letters in the word, the beginning and final letters, or whether it is a thing, a person, or a place.

If a member of a group guesses correctly, his group is next given a chance to present its own word traveler.

It would be interesting to keep a list of the word travelers which are presented in the game. Perhaps your teacher will have some one write on the board the names of the different countries. Then as each word traveler is guessed correctly, that word will be written under the name of the country from which it comes.

A Heroine of the Great Snow

PREPARATORY NOTE: Ice skating, coasting down a snow-covered hillside, snowball fights—such sports as these make us welcome a snow storm. But a snow storm can be very dangerous as you will see in this story. As you read, try to imagine how you would have felt and what you would have done if you had been one of the children in Miss Eve's school.

Danger at School

It was late February. For some days the skies had been clear and there was a promise of spring in the air. On the great Nebraska prairies, spring often came early and then, without warning, winter would return again. As Eve Evenden walked along the road to the little country school where she taught, she thought how pleasant it was to feel the warm air again. Spring was beautiful on these broad, wild prairies, which were slowly being made into farms by people who had come from across the ocean to make their homes in this new land.

Eve Evenden herself was the daughter of a struggling settler. She had grown up in a sod house and had gone to a country school and then to a summer normal school. Now, at the age of eighteen, she was teaching her first term in a little country school. Eve's pupils came from miles around, for there were not many schools on the Nebraska prairies. Every child carried a little tin pail containing his lunch of bread, potatoes, and maybe a piece of meat. The little schoolhouse, though roughly made from cheap pine lumber, was more comfortable than the sod houses where the children lived.

When Eve reached the school, a dozen children were already there. Pete Souchak had built a fire in the round stove in which they burned hay. He and his sister Mary were twisting hay into tight knots to feed the roaring stove. Coal and wood were hard to get and therefore expensive, so these early settlers used hay for fuel, even in the school house. Sometimes, in the severest cold of winter, a load of coal was bought from the railroad and used to heat the little schoolhouse.

After setting their lunch pails along the wall and hanging their wraps on the pegs at the rear, the children took their places at the tables and benches. Their own parents had made this furniture, as well as the school building itself.

Instead of paper and pencils to write with, each child had a slate and a slate pencil. Each pupil also had a reader and an arithmetic, but only the teacher had a speller. A few geographies and worn histories made up the rest of the schoolbooks. Miss Eve, as the children all called her, taught music and art without any books.

Eve rang the little bell on her desk, and the children who were playing outside came in quickly. Pupils and teacher said the Lord's Prayer together and sang "Onward, Christian Soldiers." They were then ready to begin the day's lessons.

As the third-reader class began to recite, Miss Eve noticed that the room was becoming chilly. The weather was changing, and the sky had become gray and cloudy. She asked Pete Souchak to fire up the stove again, while she went on with the reading lesson, trying not to think about the storm that was surely gathering.

When noon came the children huddled around the stove as they ate their lunch. They didn't go outdoors to play, for by this time the wind was blowing fiercely. The early morning had been so warm and springlike, thought Miss Eve, surely it was foolish to worry about bad weather. About two o'clock, however, when great white flakes began coming down, Miss Eve suddenly thought of the part of her contract which read, "In case a bad storm seems to be approaching, I promise to dismiss the children and take every precaution to see that they get safely home."

She knew that the parents did not want their children sent home unless it was necessary. For several years there had been no severe storms, only ordinary falls of snow with a few wind-blown drifts through which the children could easily make their way.

So Miss Eve kept right on with the lessons. Suddenly, in the middle of a geography lesson, she saw that it was darker outside. The air was so thick with snow that one couldn't see more than two feet ahead. Eve ran to the window, and the children quickly gathered beside her. The room had become chilly, so Pete and Mary again filled the stove with hay.

"I'm afraid this is going to be a bad storm," said Miss Eve, as she tried, without success, to peer through the whirling mass of snowflakes.

"It surely looks like it," said Jack Mintern. "George and I must go home right away. Dad is over at Holdredge and we have to get the cows in."

"I don't believe it's safe for you to go," said Miss Eve.

George and Jack, who were great strong boys of sixteen and seventeen, felt that they had no choice. There was an important task ahead of them which must be done. Eve did not stop them, and they soon disappeared into the blinding storm.

The temperature was falling rapidly and the little schoolroom was becoming very cold. The children, without being told, ran to get their wraps and put them on.

"Shall we go home, Miss Eve?" asked Willie Smith.

"I wouldn't start out in that blizzard," said Pete Souchak. "We'd better stay here until the storm stops."

"I wonder," thought Eve, "why some of the parents don't come for their children. Of course, John Mintern is away. In fact, a good many of the men went to Holdredge to that sale. Maybe they haven't had time to get back. I wonder what I should do."

A Plan for Safety

"I'm cold, Miss Eve," said little Mary Smith.

"So am I," said little Paul.

"Children," said Eve, "come over here by the stove while we decide what to do. Pete thinks we should stay here. What do you think, Mary?"

"I think so, too," said Mary. "We'd get lost before we'd gone six feet."

"Miss Eve," said Pete, "the hay is almost gone. Shall I go and get some more?"

"Not yet, Pete," said Eve. "Before you do that we must plan what we are going to do. This blizzard may be over before long, or it may last all night, but I think we had better not try to go home until the storm clears. We would be warmer in the hay shed under the hay than here in the schoolroom. Pete, do you think you can get to the shed?"

"I think so, Miss Eve. I've got my lasso, and if you'll hold on to one end of it, I'll take the other end and try to get to the shed."

The hay shed was only fifty feet from the schoolhouse, but in this blinding storm fifty feet seemed a long way. Eve took one end of the rope and stood at the door while Pete turned up his collar and started out, with the lasso tied around his waist. Eve let out the rope, a few inches at a time, while Pete struggled through the storm. Before long when he tugged on the rope, Eve began to pull it in and soon Pete appeared out of the white fog of snow.

"Couldn't find it that time," said Pete. "I'll try again."

Again he disappeared into the storm. In less than three minutes, Eve felt another tug on the rope, and again she pulled it in.

"No luck," said Pete, in a discouraged voice.

"Let me try," said Eve. "You can hold the rope for me, Pete."

As Eve tied the lasso around her waist and started out, she prayed that her good sense of direction would not fail her now. She walked slowly and carefully, with her hands stretched before her, so she would not injure herself when she reached the shed. Every minute seemed like an hour, for the cold had become almost more than she could endure. Even in her mittens, her hands had turned blue with cold.

Just as Eve was about to pull on the rope and turn back, defeated, she felt something against her fingers. Carefully, inch by inch, she made her way forward. It was a wall. She had reached the hay shed at last. No longer thinking about the cold, Eve ran her hands along the wall, first in one direction and then in the other. She soon discovered that she was at the corner of the shed. Feeling carefully along the wall, she found the door, which was shut. She opened the door, took the rope from her waist, and tied it to the wooden bar on the door. Then taking the rope in both hands, she walked sideways back toward the schoolhouse. In a few minutes she bumped into Pete at the door.

"I found it," she said, out of breath from her struggle with the storm. "You can tie the rope to that big bench by the door, Pete." Fortunately, there was plenty of rope.

"Now, children," said Eve, "how much food have you? I have a sandwich left from my lunch."

"I have three sandwiches," said Susy Smith. "I wasn't very hungry today."

Altogether there were four whole sandwiches and parts of two others—and twenty-three children to be taken care of.

"I shall take charge of the food and we will share it equally," said Eve. "We can use snow for water when we get thirsty. Now you must all wrap up carefully and join hands. Each child must hold tightly to the child in front and the child behind. If one of you should let go, all those behind him might be lost. Do you understand?"

"Yes, Miss Eve."

"The big children must look out for the little ones," warned Eve, as they started out. Mary Souchak walked directly behind Eve, holding tightly to her waist, so that both Eve's hands were free to follow the rope. With the greatest care she slid her hands along the rope, and before long they had reached the hay shed. Fortunately it had recently been packed with hay, and not much of it had been burned.

Eve called the roll and found that all the children had reached the shed safely. She wondered what had happened to the two boys who had started for home, for it was now quite dark. If only they were safe, too.

"Now we shall burrow in the hay," said Eve, "and we shall soon be warm. Each of the older children can take charge of a younger child and help to keep him as comfortable as possible." Some of the five-year-olds were crying with cold and fright.

Eve and Pete pulled a pile of loose hay into a corner and then Eve placed the children side by side in groups of two—one large child and one small child. She and Pete then piled the hay deep upon the children, leaving it loose around their heads so they could breathe. When everyone was warmly tucked in, she and Pete dug their way in beside the others and drew the hay around them.

The cold had increased greatly, but as the hay settled around them, the warmth of their bodies gradually warmed the children and after a while the cries of the smaller ones ceased.

"I'm hungry," whispered Pete Souchak, speaking softly so that only Eve could hear.

"Better be hungry than lost in the storm," whispered Eve.

"That's right," came Pete's muffled voice through the hay.

The storm outside howled with fury. In spite of the hay around them, the children were not really warm and they squirmed from time to time, trying to get comfortable. Pete pulled more hay from the top of the pile and heaped it lightly on top of the children. They pulled it close, trying to get warm.

Throughout the long night Eve could feel the bitter cold and she wondered if the children were warm, or if any of them had really frozen. But she didn't dare to pull the hay from them again to see how they were. That would only make them colder. Miserably she waited for morning to come.

The children slept fitfully, and it was well that Eve could not hear their fretful cries, which were muffled by the hay. Toward morning she nodded and slept, but before long she awoke with a sense of the cold coming around the edges of the hay. If only the children in the middle of the pile were warm, thought Eve.

Rising stiffly from her nest of hay, Eve decided to see what the conditions were outdoors. Pete Souchak got up and joined her. He, too, had slept but little.

Daylight had evidently come, but the storm still raged. The shed seemed somewhat warmer, now that the snow had piled against it. This was quite a help, for it shut out the wind.

The children began to stir, and some of them started to dig their way out. Eve decided to let them stretch a bit while she arranged the pile of hay. As the children came out from the pile, Eve found that those on the inside had been warm and comfortable. Those on the outside were tired and cross, for they had not slept well.

Eve gave each child a small bit of sandwich and some of the snow that had drifted in through the cracks of the shed. The younger children were crying and the others were far from happy, but they all gladly climbed back into the pile of hay as soon as Eve had it ready. There was no way of knowing how long the storm would last, and unless the children kept well covered up with hay, they would surely freeze to death.

The long day passed slowly. The smaller children were now crying from hunger, and the older children were cross and fretful. Eve took them beside her, one at a time, and told them to be good just a little longer. Their fathers and mothers would come after them before long.

Dreading another long night, Eve made what provisions she could. She changed the children about so that those who had been on the outside would now have their turn at the warm inner part of the pile of hay. With fitful naps the second night passed. Eve began to wonder if the storm would last forever.

After hours of napping and watching, she noticed that the wind had died down. The children in the hay seemed more comfortable. Eve herself had dozed for a little while when she was awakened by a sound from the outside—a sound very much like a cry. Dimly she heard sounds of movement.

"You there, Eve?" came a man's voice from outside the shed.

"Yes," she called.

"All the children with you?"

"Yes, all but Jack and George Mintern. They started home soon after the storm began."

"Are all the children all right?"

"Yes. They're all safe but almost starved to death."

"Thank God they are safe!"

Eve made the children stay buried in the hay while the men dug the shed out from under the snow. Then the children, wrapped in blankets, were carried to the bobsleds, where they were rolled up warmly in more blankets.

Eve did not think of herself until she tried to walk to the sled. Before she had gone six feet, she fell in a heap in the snow. Mr. Jones picked her up and wrapped her in a blanket just as if she were one of the children. When they reached the Jones's sod house, Mrs. Jones gave Eve and the children some hot soup.

"God bless you, Miss Eve, for keeping my children safe," said the happy mother while she patted Eve and cried over her, trying to realize that they all were safe at last, after the awful worry of the last two days.

After they had eaten, Eve and the children were put to bed, where they slept through the rest of the day and through the long night. The next morning they were all rested and happy again.

The great storm had passed, but it had taken its toll. Jack and George Mintern had escaped, as if by a miracle, after having been almost frozen. Many of the men had had to stay in Holdredge until the storm abated. Frantically they had gone back to their homes, expecting to find their children dead and perhaps their wives, who had gone in search of them, lost in the storm. Many people had been lost in the blizzard, and some had frozen to death. But thanks to the wisdom of Eve, their school children were all safe.

Eve was the heroine of the district, and was told that she could keep her position as teacher as long as she wanted it and that her salary would be raised at once. Many a mother kissed her, and blessed her from the depths of a grateful heart.

Many years later, when she herself was a mother, Eve often thought of the two dreadful nights in the hay shed, when the storm was raging wildly outside. She understood then how the mothers had felt when their children were brought safely home to them, and she was glad that she had been given the wisdom to know how to keep them safe.

—*Gerald Yoakam.*

Test and Study Exercises

1. Copy the sentences below that are true.
   The great storm came in December.
   Eve's father lived on a farm in Minnesota.
   Hay was used for fuel in the school stove.
   All the children were saved.

2. What does each of these groups of words below mean?

promise of spring
summer school

take every precaution
sense of direction
children slept fitfully
dimly she heard sounds

If you do not know the meanings of some of the words, or how to pronounce them, look them up in a dictionary or the word list at the back of your book.

Suggested Activities

1. Make a list of all the facts you have learned in this story. Your facts will be about school in pioneer days, dangers of weather, bravery of people, and anything else that adds to your knowledge. Arrange and number your facts in the order of their appearance in the story.

2. To add to your knowledge of the part of the country this story tells about, find other stories or books about one of these states: Nebraska, Minnesota, Wisconsin, Iowa, North Dakota, South Dakota, Kansas, Illinois. Be able to tell the class the names of the books in which you found the information.

A Boy in India

PREPARATORY NOTE: Suppose someone were to ask you, "Do your father and mother want you to attend school?" No doubt you would answer, "Why of course, they do." For in our country everyone believes it is good for boys and girls to go to school. But there are people in some places in the world who have a very different feeling about schools as you will discover when you read this story.

The First School

Something new had come to the village of Indora. The people sat on the mud veranda in front of Marati's house and talked about it until the moon rose and touched the tips of the bamboo branches with silver. Totaram and Bala, who should have gone to bed at the fall of darkness, crept behind the outer circle of grown people and listened.

71

The cause of the talk was this: that for the first time a school had come to the village. The school teacher had come from the city, and that day she had gone from house to house asking them to send their children to school.

Marati and Ganpat the Carpenter said "Yes" at once, and some of the low-caste people were glad to send their children.

But the goldsmith and some of the farmers said, "It will be a disgrace to us and broken will be our dignity when our children sit together with those from the low castes. And even if that were not the reason, we need them to help us weed the fields and to pick the cotton. And will the cows go out in the morning and care for themselves?

"And girls too! How impossible to send out girls! As though girls should not stay at home and help to prepare the day's food, or mind the babies while the women go to work in the fields. Are we rajahs that we all have servants to work for us?"

Ganpat said, "You forget that there is talk of a new law and that soon it may be that girls must wait to be married until they are much older. Indeed that will be a long time to keep them in the home. Let them go to this school, it may be that they will learn something."

And so the talk went on. Totaram was beginning to be afraid of this strange place called a school when he heard his father say, "I need my son in the fields, and my daughter must help her mother clean the rice and carry the water from the well." He was relieved and he ran off to bed.

But the next morning when the village crier beat the big drum down all the seven roads of Indora to tell them about it, and when he saw other boys and girls go into the new house just outside the village, he wished that he knew what it was all about.

Later in the day when he went with the remaining boys to take the cattle into the fields, he went and looked through the walls of the schoolhouse. These walls were made of bamboo sticks loosely woven together, and Totaram could see through the holes.

Inside he saw a strange sight. The boys and girls he knew were sitting on the floor in rows, and the teacher was making strange marks on a big blackboard with a small white stick. Totaram saw Bala and made faces at him, but Bala was interested in the marks and did not see.

"That is an odd way to spend one's time," he thought. "Our womenfolk make patterns with white dust on our front verandas. But those queer marks are not even pictures. They look like roots and creepers." And although he stood on tiptoe and pulled a bamboo stick a little aside in order to see better, he could make nothing of it.

Some weeks later he was surprised and pleased to find that Kunlik and the other boys and girls had not gone to school, but were spending the day at home and in the fields as usual. He went to ask Kunlik why not, and Kunlik looked at him sadly and said, "They have forbidden us to go.

"They say, 'You have been to school for three weeks, how is it that you cannot yet write and read?'

73

They say, 'Why is it that you bring your slates home empty at night and not full of writing?' They say, 'Your teacher is surely blindfold like the Teli's bullock or by now you would be able to tell us how much interest we should pay the money lender!' And they complain that they have wasted their money in buying our slates and our ink tables for us. Arré, they will not believe that our stomachs are full of learning but that the writing is difficult to learn. I am sorry, for I like to go to school."

The next morning the teacher came early to talk to the fathers before they left for work in the fields. They all sat on the steps of the temple of Hanuman the Monkey God under the peepul tree. Totaram was scrubbing his teeth with a neem branch beside a well, and he stopped scrubbing to listen.

"When you buy and bring home a month's rice supply from the bazaar," the teacher asked, "do you expect to eat it all in a day?" They were puzzled, but tried to look wise over it, as dogs do over a giant beetle.

But when they said "No," the teacher asked, "Then how do you expect me to fill your children's heads in three weeks with a whole year's knowledge? O wise ones! Let your children return!"

And some of the fathers shook their gray heads, some their long beards, wisely, and said, "There is some truth in it." Then they went away and did nothing.

But that night a two-wheeled cart drawn by trotting bullocks came out from the city. In it was the father of the village priest, a man so old that like the age of the banyan tree his age also was unknown. "He is so old that before the railroads came, he was," whispered the village people when they saw him. And they took the dust from his feet and called him "Dadaji" or "Honored Grandfather" out of respect. And because he was a Brahmin and belonged to the highest caste of all, some of them touched the road in front of him with their foreheads.

And it came about when they were all seated and talking peacefully, that they asked him about the school. "How comes it, Honored Grandfather, that three weeks have passed by and the teacher has not yet taught them to read? Is she not too stupid to be allowed to remain?"

And the old man laughed gently into his beard and the leaves at the top of the peepul tree which alone show the least stirring of wind, laughed with him.

"When you plant an orange tree," he asked them, "how long must you wait for it to bear fruit?"

And they answered, "Six years."

And he said, "My children, is knowledge then such a little and a worthless thing that it can be found in a day? When you are searching for a runaway buffalo do you wait until you have seen it before you give up the search? Do you believe in the man who says, 'Give him a feather and he will make you a pigeon'? Neither must you believe the one who tells you that school is the matter of a day. For it will take not one week or one month or one year, but years. O foolish ones! Let your children return to the school!"

They looked sheepish then, as dogs do when the giant beetle which they have worried has pinched them. And they gathered up their clothing about them and went away.

But Kunlik and Bala and the others returned to the school next day.

The Banyan Tree and the Money Lender

The children were back in school as usual, and Totaram, who from the encircling shadows had listened to the old Brahmin, wanted to go too. "School," he thought, "must be better than staying at home or watching the cows, or Kunlik would not like it so much." So when his mother was busy he slipped away and crept mouselike into the schoolroom at the back.

At first he could not understand it at all. The other children were ahead of him and even Bala could write his own name in big letters which looked like branches of trees. It made Totaram ashamed that the others were so much wiser than he, and he worked as hard to catch up as the squirrel people at nesting season.

The next day he went again, and the next and the next. His mother thought that he was out with the cows in the fields as usual, and asked no questions. And his father was always away at work.

After several months he could read a little and write. It took him longer to learn his language than English, because there were nearly fifty letters in the alphabet. The teacher often called his letters the tracks of birds and made him do them over again. But like the ants which carry away a grain of rice at a time until the bin is empty, he kept on learning.

One day after school when Totaram came dancing into the house like a leaf in the hot season, he found his mother turning a letter over and over in her hand. It had come from her sister in another village. The mail carrier had run with it since the time of the going out of the cows, the bells on the stick over his shoulder jingling as he ran. But the bazaar letter writer, who lived in Indora and who read and wrote all their letters for them, was away. And she sat turning it over and over because she could not read it for herself.

Before Totaram thought what he was doing he said, "Give me your letter, O my mother, and I will try to read it to you."

His mother stood surprised. "Since when have the crows adopted you and taught you wisdom?" she asked.

Totaram stood first on one foot and then on the other foot. Then he stood on both feet and looked this way and that, for he saw that he must tell the truth. Then he looked into her eyes and said, "Most revered mother, I have been going daily to the school, and while you thought that I was out with the cows, I have been learning how to read and to write."

And his mother asked, "And what did the cows do?"

And he said, "We took turns, and while half of us went to school, the others watched the cows. Then we watched the cows while they took their turn at school."

And she asked, "Have you sat and learned with the boys of the low castes and so become disgraced?"

And he hung his head like ripe wheat and said, "Yes, O Mother, but the teacher said that the harm in it was nothing."

She said sadly, "You have become as a calamity to us and your father will be angry indeed."

Then she remembered her letter and gave it to Totaram to read to her. And as he read she wondered more and more and said, "For years the letter writer has written and read my letters for me. Arré! Here my own son sits like a Brahmin scholar and reads to his mother! The times are indeed very strange."

And because she was so pleased with the news in the letter that her sister had a new son, she did not tell his father that Totaram had disobeyed him and gone to school.

Some days later it came about that Totaram's father was in trouble. Totaram knew it because he sat long hours in silence, moving no more than the big crane who waited so patiently for fish at the edge of the tank. Jai knew it because when she ran up to show him how her brass lota and plate shone in the sunlight after she had polished them with ashes, he said crossly, "Run away, child." And she had jumped away like a frightened myna bird.

Totaram remembered that he had seen a strange man with his father the night before. The man had worn the baggy trousers and colored waistcoat of the North Country, and had carried a heavy stick in his hand. Totaram did not like his looks at all.

He called Jai and they ran away to the big banyan tree to talk about it. The banyan had roots which grew out of its branches and hung down until they nearly touched the ground. These roots were tough as ropes and they began to swing on them and forgot to talk about their father's troubles.

As they were swinging Jai looked up and said, "Arré! Here comes our father and that strange man. Let us hide." And like the monkey people they climbed up the roots and lay hiding on the flat branches above.

The two men came to the tree and sat down upon a root to talk. Totaram held his breath because he was just above them.

The strange man held a paper in his hand and he said, "All that you have to do is to make a thumb

79

mark here if you cannot write your name, and then
I will lend you the fifty rupees you need."

"What does the paper say?" asked Totaram's
father.

The big man read it. "It says that in return for
fifty rupees I will pay the money lender back interest of two rupees a month until I can pay back the
entire debt."

At this point Totaram, who had been growing
more and more excited, fell off the branch to the
ground beside them, plump, like ripe fruit. And
he cried, "Father, Father, it is not true!"

And the money lender said with anger, "Will you
let a babe interfere with men's talk?"

And Totaram's father said, "My child, run home
like the squirrel you are. Indeed the Monkey God
is caring for you or you would have broken your
neck. Our talk is the talk of grown people."

But Totaram said, "I have been to the school, so I have learned to read. And this paper says that in return for one hundred rupees you agree to pay back five rupees a month until you can pay back the entire debt. And I have heard the teacher talk to the older boys about interest. And that is ten times too much!"

Then Totaram's father was indeed angry. For by the face of the money lender he could see that Totaram's words were true and that he was about to be cheated.

And the money lender slunk away like a jackal, and Totaram's father pulled Jai down out of the tree lest she fall too. And they walked home together.

His father said, "I am sorry you have been cheating, Totaram, because I want you clear like the village well, and not muddy like the stream in the nullah. But you have done me good service and saved me many months' earnings of rupees. So you are forgiven. And from tomorrow you and Jai may go to the school together with my consent. For I see that perhaps school is not such a bad thing after all."

—*Irene Mott Bose.*

Test and Study Exercises

1. What was the new thing that had come to the village of Indora?

2. When did Totaram first see the schoolhouse?

3. How did Totaram's mother learn that he had been going to school?

4. In what way was Totaram able to show his father that going to school was helpful?

5. What did the teacher say to show the people that their children could not learn everything in a short time?

6. Why did Totaram work hard to catch up with the pupils who had been in school longer than he had?

7. Look up the pronunciation and meaning of each of the following words. Then make up your own definitions of the words and add them to your vocabulary through practice.

veranda	slunk
sheepish	calamity
interfere	lender

Suggested Activity

In your geography, or history, or a reference book, find out more about India. Perhaps you would like to read about wild animals. The jungles of India are full of them. After you have read more about India, be ready to make a short oral report to the class on what you have learned.

BEAUTY
ARTISTS and IDEALS

The Search for the Beautiful

PREPARATORY NOTE: If you wanted to see the most beautiful sight in the world, where would you look for it? This is a hard question, isn't it? A question that you can't answer at once. As you read this story you will learn how a boy named Karl found the answer.

The Young Artist

There was once a boy named Karl, who lived in a little village in a valley, far from all the great cities. It was a simple and quiet village, but very pleasant to see, because of the many flowers that grew in the people's gardens, and the beautiful hills that lay just behind it. In the middle of the village was an old chapel, and as the boy's father was the sexton, their little house and garden were next door.

The chapel was a dim, restful place, with stained glass windows, which had been made hundreds of years before, and had figures of saints and angels shimmering in them. Very often, when Karl was tired of both work and play, he would go in and sit there, and would sometimes fall asleep looking at the lovely pictures in the windows.

There was a particular reason why he was so much interested in the pictures, and that was that he wished to be a great artist. Before he was old enough to read, he had drawn pictures wherever he could find a place to put them, and nothing made him so happy as to have a present of colored crayons or paints. Then, as he grew older, whatever money he could save for himself, which was not much, for his father and mother were poor, he spent in paying for lessons in drawing and painting.

But as the village was so small, Karl wished very much to go to see the world, and to study painting with great teachers. The village people thought that he was already a wonderful painter, because he could sit down before a flower, or a house or even a child's face, and make such a good copy of it that no one could think how it might be better. They could not see, therefore, why Karl was not satisfied. But he always told them that there were better pictures in the world than either he or they had ever seen, and that if they could once see them, they would never again be pleased with his.

"Well, in that case," the people answered, "why should we want to see them? If what you say is true, we would be less happy than we are now. We are pleased with your pictures, and you should be pleased with them, too."

"No," said Karl, "I cannot be pleased with anything until it is the very best I can do, and I believe I can do better. If I could only see the most beautiful things in the world, I could paint them. I have painted everything in this place, the old chapel, and the hills behind the village, and the flowers in our garden, and all the prettiest children. But all the time I have known that these are not the most beautiful sights. Somewhere is the most beautiful sight in the world. I shall never be happy till I have seen it."

Karl Finds Help

So they could not make him believe that they were right, and, although he enjoyed his work, he was never pleased with it when it was finished. At last there came a time when he thought he could go away to see the world. His brothers were now old enough to be of help to his father; and his mother, though she would be very lonely without him, seemed almost as eager as he that he should make his great journey.

There was really no one but Karl himself who knew why it was that he felt so sure he must go away. Something had happened more than a year before, which he had kept secret but had never forgotten. One day he had been working hard at a picture, as he always did in his spare minutes, and had grown tired and discouraged, because when it was finished it was not so beautiful as he had hoped. So he had gone into the little old chapel to rest and comfort himself, as I have said that he did so often.

There was one window in the chapel that Karl had always thought especially beautiful. In it was the figure of a great white angel, whom he always called the Angel of Beauty, not knowing what her real name might be. He knelt under the window, where he could look up into the face of this angel, and thought how fine it would be if she could only speak to him, and give him a message, as the angels and saints had done in earlier times.

"I know what I would say to her," he said to himself. "I would ask, 'When can I ever paint the beautiful picture that I am always trying to paint?'"

Then a very wonderful thing happened. Karl had asked this question aloud, because he was so much in earnest about it, and knew that no one else was in the chapel to hear him. Now, as he looked at the face of the angel in the window, he suddenly saw her lips open; and then before he realized what it could mean, she was speaking to him. This was what he heard: "You can paint your beautiful picture when you have seen the most beautiful sight in the world."

That was all. Karl asked more questions, and begged the angel to tell him how he could find the most beautiful sight, but she never spoke to him again, though sometimes afterward, when he would go to the little chapel to rest after a hard day's work, he would think that he saw her lips breaking into a kindly smile, as she looked down upon him in the

dim light. He never told anyone, not even his father
and mother, of the words that she had spoken to
him, but he never ceased to think of them, and this
was why he was so eager to set out on his journey,
as he did at last.

The Artist's Long Journey

It would take a very long time to tell about all of
Karl's travels, during the months that followed. On
the whole, though he saw many fine sights and made
new friends, it was a wearisome journey. He did
not have money enough to travel in comfort, and
sometimes he would find that he had spent everything he had, and would be obliged to stop somewhere for a few weeks until he could earn enough
to take him farther. Sometimes he would walk many
miles, from one city to another, and arrive there with
his feet so sore and his back so tired and aching, that
it seemed to him he wanted only one thing, his little
bed in his little room in the old home.

And all this would not have mattered, if only he
could have found the thing for which he had set out.
It always seemed to be just a little distance ahead of
him. At first he thought that he would be most likely
to find it in the galleries where the paintings and
statues of all the greatest artists were collected. So
he visited these in the different cities, and once or
twice he found a painting or a statue so wonderfully
beautiful that he exclaimed, "Surely this is the most
beautiful thing in the world!" But always some one
said to him: "No, wait till you have seen such-and-

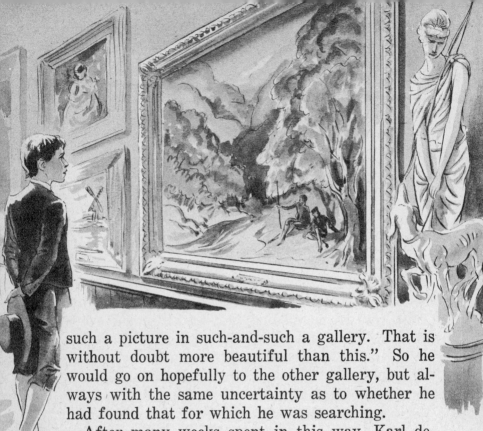

such a picture in such-and-such a gallery. That is
without doubt more beautiful than this." So he
would go on hopefully to the other gallery, but always with the same uncertainty as to whether he
had found that for which he was searching.

After many weeks spent in this way, Karl decided that it was not in pictures or statues, but in
beautiful scenes of nature, that he was most likely
to find what he sought. For whenever he saw a
lovely picture of a lake or a mountain, or a valley,
it would occur to him that if the picture were so
beautiful the landscape itself must be still more so.
As the summer was now coming on, he visited the
loveliest countries that he could hear of, where the
mountains were covered with snow the year round,
while the valleys between were filled with wonderful
flowers, and brooks went singing down the slopes
and emptied themselves into lakes as blue as the sky.

He had never dreamed of anything so beautiful as some of these places, yet the same thing happened that had happened before. Whenever he would say to another traveler that he thought this must be the most beautiful sight in the world, the traveler would say, "No. I have seen one still better; you will find it in the Valley of So-and-so." Then Karl would take up his journey again, always with new hope.

Karl Gets Bad News

Meantime he did not get good news from home. His mother wrote him that his father was dead, and this made him very sad. Then she wrote that it had been a hard winter in their neighborhood, so that his brothers had found it difficult to earn as much as usual, and they had had to sell some of their land to buy fuel to keep them warm. But she did not ask Karl to come home, for she was as anxious as he was that he should become a great artist, and was sure that he would succeed if he only had good luck on his journey. So she told him to go on, and not be troubled about the things that were happening at home, for she would not have written of them at all if it had not been to explain why she could not send him any money.

So Karl continued his journey a little farther, and tried to keep a good heart. At last he felt more certain than ever before that he was going to find the object of his search, for a number of travelers had told him that he ought to go to see a certain castle on a certain mountain, in a certain distant country, where the view was undoubtedly the most beautiful in the world. So many people told him this, that Karl felt now that all he had to do was to get money enough to take him to that country, and his search would be ended. But this was hard to do. So he stopped in the city where he was, and found regular work, copying little pictures for a man who sold them. All the money he earned, he saved for the expense of his journey.

One day, when he thought that he had almost enough, he received a letter. It was from the village where his home was, but not from his mother. A neighbor wrote to him, telling him that his mother was too sick to write for herself, and that his brothers were sick, too; for there was a fever in their valley, and half the people in the village were ill. The neighbor said that he did not think Karl's mother would die, if she had good care, and that he was doing all he could for her and for the brothers, but there was no money with which to buy good food or medicines for them, and their near friends were almost as poor as they. So he had decided to write, although Karl's mother would not agree to it, asking him to come home.

It was hard to receive a letter like this, when he was almost ready to finish the journey that had been so long and hard. Karl thought about it for a long time; but of course decided that there was but one thing to do. He must go home where his mother needed him. He was now not so very far away, and the money that he had saved for the longer journey would be enough to buy many comforts for the sick ones. So he bade good-by to the man who had employed him, and took the quickest way he could find toward home.

Although it had been a little hard to change his plans, when Karl was once on his way home it was surprising how happy he felt about it. He did not know how much he had missed his mother and his brothers and the old place until his face was turned toward them again. So instead of feeling sad about going in that direction, he could hardly wait to see the little village; and when he had really arrived there, he could not wait to get a sight of his mother, but ran down the street as fast as his feet would carry him, until he reached the door of their little house. There was his mother at the door to meet him, for she was recovering from the fever, and through the window had seen him running down the street.

Then Karl told her about his journey, and why he had come home; that he had not yet found the most beautiful sight in the world, but that he now felt more than willing to wait for it. "For," said he, "I have seen many beautiful things, and I can make pictures of them. Some day I may be able to finish the journey. But I am so happy to be at home again and to see you, that I do not feel now as if I cared about anything else."

The End of the Search

Then his mother took him by the hand, and they walked together out into the little garden, where everything was gay with the late summer flowers. "Why, dear me!" said Karl, "I never knew that we had such a beautiful little garden! Have you changed it any since I have been away?"

"No," said his mother, "but it has grown a little better every year, even when left to itself."

"It is certainly the prettiest garden I have ever seen," said Karl. "And look at that view of the hills behind the village! How beautiful it is with the afternoon lights and shadows lying on it! Mother, was that view of the hills always there just in the same way?"

"I think it must have been," said his mother, smiling at him. "You always thought it was a beautiful sight, Karl."

"Yes," said Karl, "but not half so wonderful as this. And you, too, mother, you have grown lovelier than you ever were before, in spite of having been sick and poor. If I were a great artist, I would paint your portrait and make my fortune by it."

His mother smiled again, not believing what he said, but pleased that he should think so.

"Mother," said Karl again, "I will paint your picture, sitting here in the garden, with the flowers blossoming about you, and the view of the hills behind you. If I can only make it seem as beautiful to others as it does to me, it will be the best picture I have ever made."

So the next morning Karl made his mother sit in the garden, and then brought his paints and went to work. He was afraid that everything would not look so beautiful as it had the night before, when he had first come home, but it did. He worked faster and more joyfully than he had ever worked before, hoping that he would be able to put into the picture the wonderful new beauty that he saw all around him.

At sunset the picture was almost finished, and Karl sat alone in front of it, for his mother had gone into the house to get supper. He was feeling a little tired and discouraged, as he always did after a long day's work. Perhaps, he thought, it would be impossible for him to make other people see what he was seeing, and the picture would be nothing, after all, but a pleasure to his mother and himself. Perhaps it would mean nothing to others.

"As soon as it gets too dark to work on it any longer," he said, "I shall go into the chapel to see my Angel of Beauty. I am sure she will comfort me, as she always used to do when I was discouraged."

Just then he thought he heard some one beside
him, and when he looked up quickly, there stood the
white angel at his side, just as he had seen her so
often in the chapel window! Karl was so surprised
that he could not think of anything to say, but sat
looking up at her with big, wondering eyes.

"I have been here helping you all day," she said,
"but I thought it would comfort you more if you
could see me." Then she touched his hand lightly
with her hand, and Karl went to work again with
his brush, which now seemed to do its work with a
wonderful skill that he had never noticed in it before.

"Ah," he said happily, "that was the color I wanted all the time! And that is the light on the hills that I saw last evening and thought so beautiful!"

Then, resting from his work a minute, he turned his face again toward the angel, and said to her, "Will this really be the picture that I have wanted to paint for so long?"

"Yes," said the angel, "it will; for at last you have found the most beautiful sight in the world."

"And it was here all the time?" said Karl.

"What is here does not make the picture," said the angel, "but what you see." Then she faded away as quietly as she had come, and Karl saw that his picture was finished.

This was the picture that made all the world know that Karl was a great artist, but how it came to be painted has never before been told.

—*Raymond M. Alden.*

Test and Study Exercises

1. Make as many small words as you can out of the words in the list below. Write your small words on a piece of paper.

village	chapel	windows
particular	nothing	father
painted	enjoyed	finished
comfort	earnest	greatest

97

2. What was Karl looking for?

3. Where did Karl find what he was looking for?

Suggested Activity

Think of the following sentences as steps in Karl's life as told in this story. These steps are not in order now. On a piece of paper write them in the correct order and number them. Then you will have an outline of the story.

Karl hears bad news.

Karl studies the chapel windows.

Karl looks in the art galleries.

The artist finds what he looked for.

Karl begins his search.

The artist studies nature.

The artist paints village people.

Day

PREPARATORY NOTE: As you read this poem, try to remember sights you have seen that are like the ones described here.

This is the way the morning dawns,
Rosy tints on flowers and trees;
Winds that wake the birds and bees,
Dewdrops on the flowers and lawns—
This is the way the morning dawns.

This is the way the sun comes up,
Gold on brooks and grass and leaves;
Mists that melt above the sheaves,
Vine and rose and buttercup—
This is the way the sun comes up.

This is the way the daylight dies,
Cows are lowing in the lane,
Fireflies wink o'er hill and plain,
Yellow, red, and purple skies—
This is the way the daylight dies.

—*Anonymous*.

Test and Study Exercises

1. Make a list, in pairs, of all the words that rhyme, or sound alike—for example, trees and bees.

2. Which of the word pictures in the poem do you like best?

A Great Child Musician

PREPARATORY NOTE: If you saw a little boy three years old climbing up to a piano, you would expect to hear a rather bad noise. But as you read of the three-year-old boy in this story, you will be surprised, especially when you know that the story is true.

"Please! Father, won't you teach me, too?" asked little three-year-old Wolfgang in his baby voice. He had been listening quietly and carefully while Nannerl, his older sister, was having her first piano lesson.

"Wait until you grow up a little bit, Wolfgang," said his father, who was an important musician in Austria. It was his wish that both of his children should share his great love for music. "You are so small, my son, you can hardly reach the piano keys now."

"But I want to learn," pleaded the little boy.

"And you shall learn, my little Wolfgang, as soon as you are old enough."

Leopold Mozart continued with his daughter's piano lesson, while Wolfgang stood beside Nannerl and watched every move she made. When her lesson was over and she had left the piano, the little boy got upon the piano bench and began to repeat what his sister had played. One after another he played all the exercises that Nannerl had been taught.

Wolfgang's father and mother could hardly believe their eyes and ears. How was it possible that a three-year-old child, hardly more than a baby, could play like this? They were sure, now, of one thing. The little boy must have the lessons for which he had begged.

Little Wolfgang scarcely had to be told anything, for he seemed to know without lessons just what to do. One day, two years later, Leopold Mozart and another of the court musicians, discovered little Wolfgang busy writing music. The paper seemed to be covered with ink spots, but when the little boy played what he had written, the men were astonished. Wolfgang had written a minuet that was perfect in every way. It was plain to both of these musicians that the child was a genius.

Wolfgang soon learned to play the violin also. Before long he could play either the first or the second violin parts with his father and their friends. Many people came to the Mozart home to hear this gifted child musician. Until they had seen and heard for themselves, they would not believe the stories they had heard about his playing.

Meanwhile his sister, Nannerl, had also been making excellent progress in her music. So their father now decided to make use of the musical genius of his children. He would travel with them all over Europe and give concerts which would bring them money as well as renown.

They journeyed first to Linz and then to Vienna. At a monastery in Ips, little Wolfgang astonished the monks by playing the great organ as if he had always known how. Yet he had never even seen an organ before. At Vienna the boy played for the emperor, Franz Joseph, who called him, "My little magician." Here Wolfgang played with the piano keys covered. He delighted the court and won the hearts of both the emperor and the empress with his playing. The popularity of Wolfgang and Nannerl increased in Vienna, and finally the emperor gave each of them a beautiful diamond ring.

The next year the children went to Paris, and on the way they stopped at many towns and cities to play. During the months they were in Paris, they played before the French court, where everyone was charmed and delighted with them.

After leaving Paris the children went to London, where they played before the king. He became greatly interested in Wolfgang when he heard him play difficult pieces by Bach and Handel which the boy had never seen before.

On June 5, 1764, the king's birthday, the Mozart children gave their first public concert in London.

It was a great success, and they earned one hundred guineas. Soon after this they played again at court and won great applause by playing a piano duet. In those days a piano duet was something quite new and unusual.

The children gave many concerts in England and in other parts of Europe before they finally returned home, two years later. Wolfgang's father then decided that the boy must study music in Italy, which at that time was the leading musical nation of the world.

Wolfgang was greatly interested in the colorful beauty of Italy, especially its blue lakes and the gay costumes of the peasants and soldiers. Everything was quite different from Austria and England. Above all, the boy loved the great churches, with their wonderful organs.

During Holy Week, Wolfgang and his father went to Rome, where they heard the celebrated Miserere in the Sistine Chapel. This sacred piece was never

given in any other place in the world. The boy was so deeply moved upon hearing this glorious music that he could not sleep that night. The music kept going through his mind. Finally he got up and began to write the notes of the musical score of the Miserere, whose beauty had filled his soul. All night long he worked, and when morning came he had fallen asleep, with his head resting on the table. But he had completed the entire score of the Miserere.

When Wolfgang went the next day to hear the Miserere again, he carried the music in his hat. On hearing the piece a second time he found that he had made only a few slight mistakes in writing it from memory. When the people of Rome heard what Wolfgang had done, they were amazed. Such a thing was unknown in the history of music. This lad from Austria was indeed a genius, they said.

Wolfgang and his father traveled through Italy, and the boy received the highest praise and the most respectful attention wherever he went. When he returned to Rome he was given the Order of the Golden Spur by the Pope. From this time on, he had the right to be addressed as the Chevalier de Mozart.

While in Milan, young Mozart wrote his first opera, in the short period of three months. This opera was performed in Milan, and was conducted by Wolfgang himself. It was a great success. As a result, Mozart was given high honors and requested to write some music for a royal wedding.

After all of his travels and triumphs Wolfgang finally returned home. The hopes of his father and the dreams of his mother had more than come true by the time Wolfgang was a young man. Their Wolfgang, whose baby fingers had charmed the musical world with their skill on piano and organ, was now recognized as one of the great writers of music of all time. They had done their work well, and they were happy as well as proud. Their Wolfgang would delight the whole world with his music.

—*Gerald Yoakam.*

Test and Study Exercises

1. How old was Wolfgang when he first asked his father to teach him?

2. What made Mozart's father and mother sure that their son should have music lessons?

3. How did Mozart astonish the monks in the monastery at Ips?

Suggested Activity

Find another book that tells something about Mozart. Be ready to tell the name of the book and a few facts you found in it about Mozart.

Your Own Music Box

PREPARATORY NOTE   Read this story to find how you can make music without playing a musical instrument.

In the story which you have just been reading, Wolfgang Mozart was able to bring beautiful music from a wooden frame with keys, pedals, and many strings, called a piano.

Not all of us can do that, but you and I each have a voice box inside our throats; and from that voice box we can bring beautiful sounds and pleasing melodies. Your voice box is your music box, you know.

If you have not done so before, begin right now listening to the voices of the people all around you. Remember, though, that they are also listening to you! Soft voices . . . loud voices . . . sweet voices . . . harsh voices . . . low voices . . . high voices . . . happy voices . . . sad voices . . . musical voices . . . and those which seem to play just one tune! All of the music boxes in the throats are sending out their tones. You know your friends partly by their voices, don't you? Your friends also know you.

The piano that Wolfgang played upon so well had a scale of eight notes, repeated many times. His violin had only four strings. But *your* music box can make many more sounds than these. How many do you think? Ten? Twenty? Thirty? More than that! Your voice can make forty different sounds.

Your voice box has only two strings instead of the four strings of the violin, but these two can do some things which violin strings can never do. They can grow shorter and longer by themselves. They can become thinner or thicker according to the way you *feel*—sad or happy, tired or gay. The two strings in your music box are called *vocal cords*.

The four strings of the violin are different in thickness, and they have to be shortened by the fingers of the player. The vocal cords within your music box are much more wonderful. They can adjust themselves. You don't have to stop and think just how your music box will work; but if you wish to make sounds more musical and beautiful than any you have made before, you must practice just as Wolfgang had to practice on his piano and violin. Let us try.

Some of the sounds of our speech are singing sounds which seem to hum or sing a little tune. They are *m*, *n*, and *ng*. Say *humming*, *singing*, *ringing*, *ding-dong*. Can't you hear the music from your music box as you say them? When you say *murmur*, can't you hear the music of the brook that goes murmuring along? Doesn't *tinkle* sound like the tinkle of a bell? And doesn't the word *minuet* seem to dance for you?

Just like the piano, the organ, and the violin, your voice box can sound high notes and low notes. As you say *skipping*, *clicking*, *silver*, *city*, and other words with short vowels, your voice is lighter, isn't it? As you say *golden*, *moon*, *calm*, and *mountain*, you are bringing the deeper notes from your music box. Can you think of other soprano words, and other alto words—those with higher, lighter tones; and those with deeper, darker tones?

Out of your music box comes your voice with the same properties as other musical instruments: *pitch*, which may be high, low, or medium; *volume*, which means loudness or softness of tone; *quality*, which may be pleasing or harsh; and the power of making the tone last for a long time or a short time. This is called *duration*. What a wonderful instrument your own music box is!

—*Louise Abney.*

Test and Study Exercises

1. Study the words in the list below. Then write on your paper these headings: singing words, high note words, low note words. Under each heading put the words that belong there.

humming	mountain	minuet
tinkle	clicking	golden
moon	singing	calm
ringing	silver	ding-dong

The Little Boy Who Loved Trees

PREPARATORY NOTE: Mozart's beautiful music made him famous. Corot was famous for producing beauty of another kind. Read this story to learn what kind of beauty that was and how Corot worked to create it.

The Boy Corot

There once lived a man who thought springtime the most beautiful season of the year. His name was Camille Corot. He was never so happy as when close to Mother Nature. He used to talk to the birds. They seemed to sing more sweetly when he came into the woods.

Camille Corot was born in Paris in 1796. His father was a tradesman. Everything was very cozy in the Corot home. The father did well in his trade, so he had plenty of money to make his family comfortable.

In the summer time the Corot family did not stay in Paris. They had a pretty little home in the country. Near the house was a large pond. Camille was always glad to leave the hot, dusty streets of Paris. It was so cool and shady under the trees by the pond.

Camille's full name was Jean Baptiste Camille Corot. Children in France often have as many names as that. In the seven years of his school life, our little friend was always called Camille. We, too, shall call him by that name.

When summer came each year, how glad Camille was to put away his books! It seemed good to be with his father and mother once more. Soon after the close of school, the whole family went to the country. Then, indeed, was the boy happy. He knew all the trees about the country home. They were his friends. The birds, the flowers, the pure air, and the blue skies all gave him pleasure.

He spent the whole day out-of-doors. When it grew dark, he was sorry to go into the house. When all the family were asleep, he used to sit by the open window in his room. What beautiful pictures he saw in the outside world!

Camille sometimes sat for hours watching the silvery moon travel across the skies. He fancied that the moon was a shepherdess and that the fleecy white clouds were her sheep. Often the wind drove the clouds far apart. Then he would wonder if the shepherdess could ever get her flock together again.

All was so still at night. Nothing could be heard but the rustling of the leaves. Then the little dreamer at the window fancied that the trees were whispering secrets to one another.

As he looked out into the night, Camille thought the fairies were having a party. He thought he saw them come sailing across the pond on the floating leaves. He fancied that the fairies danced under the trees. The fireflies were their lanterns. The harebells made their music.

When Camille was seventeen, he became a clerk in a dry goods store. His father hoped that he would like the trade. He wished his son to be a rich cloth merchant some day.

Camille did not like to stay in the store all day. He was happier out-of-doors where he could hear the birds sing. On his holidays he used to take, long walks. He wandered along the banks of the river and out into the fields and woods.

When he was about twenty years old, he began to draw the things he saw on his walks. Then it was that the merchant saw his counters covered with papers. Then it was that Camille used every spare moment for drawing. He wished that he might work with a brush instead of a yardstick.

He always carried a sketchbook in his pocket when he went walking. He filled the pages with drawings of trees and flowers. He made sketches of the river winding through the meadows and of the soft fleecy clouds. He set up an easel in the corner of his bedroom. He spent many pleasant hours there. He filled in his sketches with color.

Young Corot made friends with an artist. This friend helped Corot with his drawing. The artist taught Corot how to mix the colors. He showed him how to lay on the paint.

Now Corot wished to leave the cloth merchant's shop. His father at first was unwilling. At last he gave his consent. How happy Corot was that he no longer had to measure cloth and tie up bundles!

The first day he was free, Corot took his easel and brushes and started off to paint. He was crossing a bridge. He saw the city in the distance. He thought, "How beautiful that looks! I'll make a picture of it."

Corot was well liked in his father's shop. The girls who worked there ran down to the bridge to watch him paint. "Look, Rosa," one said, "see the shadows in the water. Is not Camille a wonderful artist?"

Corot's artist friend died. After his death Corot went to another teacher. This man was a landscape painter. Landscapes were just what Corot enjoyed painting more than anything else. He was happy in his work with this teacher.

Manhood of Corot

In 1825 Corot went to Italy to study. The artists there liked him. He had a good voice for a song. He could tell a story well. He was always ready for a good time. Though they liked Corot, they laughed at his pictures.

One day Corot was painting a picture of a fine old building in Rome. One of the artists told him that the work was well done. This was the first praise that Corot had received in Italy.

Soon after this all the artists were at dinner together. The one who had praised Corot's work arose. He said, "We have all been laughing at Corot's paintings. But I tell you that he may some day be the master of us all."

When he returned to France, Corot worked very
hard. A great many years passed before he sold a
single picture. His paintings were different from
those of other French artists. People did not care
to buy them. It did not make Corot unhappy because
his pictures were not sold.

He was always laughing or singing. He was up
with the birds every morning. Early in the day he
started out to the woods. On these trips he wore
a great straw hat, and carried an umbrella under
his arm.

He would talk to the birds and trees and butter-
flies as he went along. "Is it for me you are singing
little bird?" he would say. "Well, this is fine."

In his studio Corot wore a loose blue blouse. A gay red and white striped cap was on his head. Here he sang all day at his work. When night came he would say, "Well, I must stop. My Heavenly Father has put out my lamp."

Often Corot went into the country to sketch. Sometimes he stayed all day. If he did well at his work, he went home pleased. He would say to his mother, "A little fairy came to me today. She touched me with her wand and gave me success."

Often he was sad when he returned at night. Then his mother would ask with kindness, "Has not the little fairy been to see you today?"

On Sunday mornings Corot always went with his mother to church. He said he was proud to walk down the street with her. He always spoke of her as "the beautiful woman."

Paris was the home of the artist in the winter months. In the springtime he went to his father's country home. The moonlight glimmering on the pond, the great trees, and the soft clouds were just as beautiful to him now as when he was a boy living among these natural friends.

When April came, Corot was never in Paris. His friends knew that he had gone to the country to watch the birds. These little creatures were not afraid of this gentle man. They seemed to know that he was their friend. Corot used to say, "The birds perch on the branches above me to watch my work."

In 1827 one of Corot's pictures was hung in a large art gallery of Paris. From that time until his death his pictures were shown there every year. Yet no one cared to buy them.

About this time there was a war in France. Corot hated war. When the siege of Paris began, he left the city. During the siege many of the soldiers were wounded. Many nurses were needed to care for the sick and dying. Then Corot returned to Paris. During the whole siege he helped to care for the soldiers. Some of his loveliest pictures were painted during these dreary weeks.

For forty years Corot had been painting. At the end of that time his pictures were greatly admired. In 1867 he received a great honor. He was given the cross of the Legion of Honor.

When Corot's pictures were first hung in the art galleries, people hardly noticed them. Later, some of the artists not only praised but bought his paintings. Soon other people became interested in them. By and by they began to buy Corot's landscapes.

Crowds of people visited his studio. Corot found that he could not get his work done on account of his many visitors. He decided to have one day each week in which to welcome his friends. After this, company came only upon the appointed day.

In his old age many people in Paris called him Father Corot. No one was more beloved than he. No wonder, for no man was more kind and gentle. No man was more ready to help those in trouble. Sometimes he gave money. Sometimes he gave words of cheer and wise advice.

Corot gave to all the beggars who came to him. He never turned one away empty-handed. Sometimes as many as twenty-five beggars came to his door in one day.

One New Year's day Corot was walking down the street. He met an old man begging. Corot gave him a piece of silver and went on. When he had gone a few steps he turned back. He hurried after the old man. Corot put ten pieces of silver into the beggar's hand. "Today all the world receives presents, so you must have yours, too," said the artist.

All the children loved Father Corot. He was their good friend. He liked to plan surprises for them. At Christmas time he prepared baskets for the children who lived in his neighborhood. The artist filled the baskets with nuts and fruit, with candy and toys. Would you not like to have lived near Father Corot?

Many pupils came to Corot to study. He was glad to teach them what he knew about painting. He would take no pay for the lessons he gave.

We have told you nothing about the kind of pictures that this gentle artist made. He did not care to paint animals as Rosa Bonheur did. He did not often paint people as Millet was so fond of doing. He

116

loved nature—the trees and the skies, the dewy meadows and clear lakes. He liked to represent springtime, when all the world is freshly dressed in green.

In his pictures Corot liked especially to show trees. He was very fond of trees with delicate branches and leaves that tremble in the breeze. Such trees we often see in his paintings. Such trees we see in his picture called *The Willows*.

Many times Corot thought of the poor men in the prisons. He wished that they might see the country. He thought that they would become good men if they could see nature as he saw it. Every flower, every blade of grass, and every singing bird spoke to him of God.

"I wish that I might paint the walls of a prison," said Corot. "I would have the blue sky and the clouds. I would have the trees lifting their branches toward Heaven. I am sure that the prisoners would then think of the loving kindness of God and obey his laws."

When Corot was an old man, his friends gave a banquet in his honor. They presented him with a gold medal. They said many kind things when they gave it to him. Corot was not expecting this. His heart was so full of happiness that tears came to his eyes. He could only whisper, "It makes me very happy to be loved so much." This was the last time that the artist was away from home.

When Corot died all France mourned for him. The people felt that they had lost a gentle, loving friend.

—*Olive Horne and Katherine Scobey.*

Test and Study Exercises

1. Copy the sentences below that are true. There are four of them.

Corot's full name was Jean Baptiste Camille Corot.

Corot was a famous English painter.

Corot was a kind man.

Corot loved trees.

Corot was a famous French artist.

Suggested Activities

1. Find another book that tells something about Corot. Write down the name of the book.

2. Be able to tell in your own words everything the sentences below say.

All was so still at night. Nothing could be heard but the rustling of the leaves. Then the little dreamer at the window fancied that the trees were whispering secrets to one another.

The Troublesome Twins

PREPARATORY NOTE: Read this story to see how much prettier words sound when they are pronounced correctly.

Jack Careless and Jane Indifferent are the troublesome twins of the Word family. Because of their poor speech habits, they frequently get some little word into trouble. Jack Careless is discourteous because he slights certain members of the family. He leaves out sounds that really should be included. He says *fam'ly* for *family*, and *hist'ry* for *history*. He is very careless, indeed!

Jack's twin sister, Jane, just doesn't care about her speech. She thinks it doesn't matter how she talks, or what her friends or family think about her words. That's why she is called indifferent.

Both of the twins hurry so much that they stumble over important little letters in everyday words. And they pay almost no attention to syllables when they use the following words: *poem* (which has two syllables, not one, you know), *mirror*, *nearer*, *error*, *jewel* and *orange*.

Here are the words which the twins neglect. When *you* pronounce them, be sure to sound the letters which the troublesome twins leave out, and be sure to watch the syllables. Just for fun you might guess which of the letters the twins neglect; but put them all in yourself!

about	arithmetic
across	around
arctic	because

before   particular
caramel   perhaps
electric   poinsettia
electricity   probably
eleven   really
every   refrigerator
family   suppose
generally   surprise
geography   temperature
government   usually
history   valuable
ivory   violet
miserable   violin

Test and Study Exercises

1. Why is Jack, in this story, called *Jack Careless*?

2. Why is Jane called *Jane Indifferent*?

3. Make a list of any other words that you or anyone you know does not say correctly.

4. Why do you think it is worth while to be careful when you speak?

Mockery

PREPARATORY NOTE: Look carefully at the picture on this page. Then see how the word pictures in the poem are like it. Think, too, of how many of these things you have really seen yourself.

Happened that the moon was up before I went to
    bed,
Poking through the bramble trees her round, gold
    head.
I didn't stop for stocking,
I didn't stop for shoe,
But went running out to meet her—oh, the night
    was blue!

Barefoot down the hill road, dust beneath my toes;
Barefoot in the pasture smelling sweet of fern and
    rose!
Oh, night was running with me,
Tame folk were all in bed—
And the moon was just showing her wild, gold head!

But before I reached the hilltop, where the bramble
    trees are tall,
I looked to see my lady moon—she wasn't there at
    all!—
Not sitting on the hilltop,
Nor slipping through the air,
Nor hanging in the brambles by her bright, gold
    hair!

I walked slowly down the pasture and slowly up
    the hill,
Wondering and wondering, and very, very still.
I wouldn't look behind me,
I went at once to bed—
And poking through the window was her bold, gold
    head!

—Katherine D. Riggs.

Test and Study Exercises

1. Who or what was "poking through the window"
with her "bold, gold head"?

2. How many of the things the poet tells about can
you find in the picture on page 121?

3. How would you say this line to show surprise? "I
looked to see my lady moon—she wasn't there at all!"

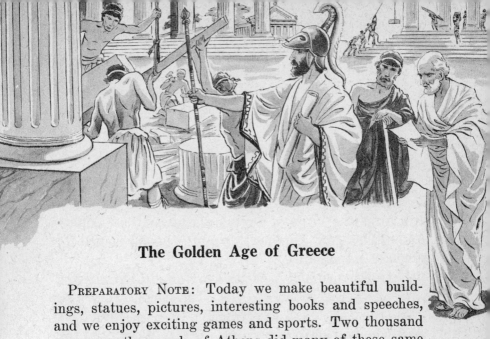

The Golden Age of Greece

PREPARATORY NOTE: Today we make beautiful buildings, statues, pictures, interesting books and speeches,
and we enjoy exciting games and sports. Two thousand
years ago the people of Athens did many of these same
things. Read this story to learn of the builders and artists, the writers and speakers, and the athletes of ancient
Athens.

A Great Man of Athens

Their city had been burned to the ground by
enemies, but the people of Athens, in old Greece, began at once to rebuild it. Soon it was more beautiful and more powerful than ever before. During this
time the city grew with great rapidity and became
more and more important throughout the world.

It was at this time that Athens chose Pericles for
its leader. Fortunately, he was a truly great man.
He was not only wise, but he was also an able ruler.
Although he came from a wealthy family, he was
interested in the good of the common people.

123

Instead of ruling the people without giving them a chance to express an opinion, Pericles always found out what they thought and wanted. Because the people had found him to be honest, they usually voted for the laws that he favored. Thus he had more power than most kings.

The people trusted Pericles so much that they kept him in office for thirty years. This period is known as the "Age of Pericles" and as the "Golden Age of Greece." During this age Athens reached its greatest importance.

Under the rule of Pericles everyone in Greece was sure of having enough to eat. The people were also given their rights in government. For the first time men who helped in governing the city were paid for their work. This enabled the poor to take part in their government. Until now only the rich had been able to give any time to government.

During the Age of Pericles, Athens became the most important city in the ancient world. Its navy was more powerful and its trade was larger than that of any other city. From far and near Athenian merchant ships brought wealth. Two hundred fifty cities came under the power of Athens and paid taxes to the city. Large sums of money poured into the city's treasury.

Many kinds of new business also sprang up in Athens at this time. Since the people were wealthier than ever before, they became more extravagant and wanted to buy many new things. To supply the people's wants, more and more craftsmen and artists were kept busy. Potters, jewelers, weavers, shoemakers, builders, furniture makers, and many others worked hard to make the goods that were needed.

The Beauty of Athens

During the Age of Pericles, Athens was not only powerful and rich, but it also became the most beautiful city the world had ever seen. Because Pericles loved Athens, he wanted to make it beautiful. For this reason, he asked the people to vote money for fine buildings. This they did.

Many of these buildings were built on the Acropolis. This was a high, rocky hill in the center of Athens. Here Pericles built a number of temples of great splendor and beauty as well as altars in honor of the gods. Of these temples, the most beautiful was the Parthenon. It was built in honor of Athena, the goddess of wisdom.

Although the builders of the Parthenon followed a simple style, it was so beautiful that people are still using it as a model. The Parthenon was made of white marble and had a wide porch on all four sides. The roof was held up by graceful columns, also made of clear, white marble. Above these columns was a border of marble, beautifully carved. These carvings are among the most famous in the world. They may now be seen in the British Museum in London, England.

Pericles also had a splendid theater built on the Acropolis. This theater was so large that it could seat all the freemen in the city at one time. Here the people were entertained by plays, dancing, and music. Because Pericles thought that the people could learn from plays, he gave free seats to the poor. So everyone in Athens was able to go to the theater whenever he liked.

Besides its altars, its temples and other beautiful buildings, the Acropolis was famous for its beautiful statues. Some of the best of these were statues of the goddess Athena. They were carved by the great sculptor Phidias. One of them was about seven times as high as a grown man and stood inside the Parthenon. The face, hands, and feet were made of ivory, and the dress of glistening gold.

Another large statue of Athena stood near the entrance to the Acropolis. It was nearly twice as high as the statue inside the Parthenon and could be seen by the sailors far out at sea. Phidias, who made these statues, was one of the greatest sculptors the world has ever known.

Pericles also had many beautiful buildings made in other parts of Athens. The market place was a beautiful square which had temples and other handsome buildings on all sides. Although many of the buildings of old Athens have disappeared and others are in ruins, we know that the Athenians were among the greatest builders in all the world.

Greek art of every kind was at its best during the Age of Pericles. No other people have ever excelled the Athenian artists of that day. Some of them made beautiful vases, bowls, jars, and other kinds of pottery. These were usually decorated with paintings. Much Greek pottery has come down to us and may now be seen in the museums of the world. It is some of the finest ever made.

Although we no longer have any of the pictures which the Greeks painted, we are told that they were exquisite. That the statues carved by the Greeks were beautiful we are quite sure, for some of them may still be seen.

As you know, Phidias was the greatest of all the Greek sculptors. Besides his famous statues of Athena, he also carved a large statue of Zeus and another of Aphrodite. Unfortunately, his statue of Zeus, which came to be called one of the "Seven Wonders of the Ancient World," has been destroyed. The statue of Aphrodite is one of the most famous in the world today. Another well-known Greek statue is called the "Winged Victory." Although the head and arms have been lost, it is still beautiful.

Other Great Men of Athens

During the Age of Pericles the Athenians were also interested in many kinds of writings, or literature. It was at this time that the poems of Homer were first written down. It was also at this time that other Greek writers wrote their best works. Some of these writers wrote poetry, and others wrote histories or geographies. It is from such writings that we have learned much that we know about the ancient world.

Among the other writers of ancient Athens were several poets who wrote plays. Many of their plays are among the finest ever written. They are still read and are sometimes even given in our theaters today.

Athens was also famous for its wise men. Of all these, one of the greatest was Socrates, the teacher of truth and goodness. Although Socrates had many pupils, he did not teach in a school. Instead he taught in the street, in the market place, or in any other place where young men were likely to be found.

Most of all, Socrates endeavored to help his pupils to think clearly and to see the truth. He taught that man must be good to be happy. He often said that he himself was wiser than other men only because he understood how little he really knew.

Of course, Socrates made many enemies, for most people do not like to be shown how little they know. Sometimes he scoffed at the religion of the Greeks, for he did not believe in their many gods and goddesses. In fact, Socrates believed in one God, as we do today.

At last Socrates' enemies said that he did not worship the Greek gods and that he taught harmful ideas to the young men of Athens. So a trial was held, and Socrates was ordered to put himself to death by drinking poison.

Among the pupils of Socrates was one man who was to become as famous as his teacher. This was Plato. Plato wrote down many of the things Socrates had taught him. In this way he saved for the world many of the sayings and ideas of that great thinker.

Plato also wrote down many of his own ideas. Although he lived more than two thousand years ago, we still believe much that he said about life. He was, indeed, one of the world's greatest thinkers and one of the best writers who ever lived. Among the many things which he gave to the world was a new system of education.

Like Socrates, Plato also taught many of the young men of Athens and had a number of brilliant pupils. The brightest of them all was Aristotle, who also became a great thinker and a great teacher. Most people think that he was one of the greatest teachers the world has ever known. Through his writings we have learned many things, for Aristotle wrote on many different subjects. Today Socrates, Plato, and Aristotle are considered three of the wisest men who ever lived.

Since Athens was ruled by the freemen of the city, almost everybody who lived there was interested in government. Wherever men gathered, they talked about government matters. Much of this talking took place in meetings, called assemblies. Here the people went to talk about the laws that were needed. Here, too, they met to vote and to decide many important matters.

When a man had an idea that he wanted Athens to accept, he talked to the men in the assemblies. If he could make a good speech, he was likely to make the people think that he was right. So many Greeks tried to become good speakers, or orators as they are called.

Although there were many great orators in Athens, none was more famous than Demosthenes. As a boy he stuttered and stammered so that he could scarcely be understood. Whenever he talked

before the boys at school, he spoke so poorly that
they laughed at him. This only caused him to be
more nervous than ever.

All this might have stopped a less courageous person. But Demosthenes did not easily give up to
failure. Going to the beach every day, he took a
handful of pebbles, put them into his mouth, and
said his speeches to the roaring ocean waves. He
kept this up until he was able to speak clearly. Then
he went into the assemblies and spoke to the people
there. What he said was not only interesting but
the way in which he said it was also forceful. Thus
he became the greatest orator of his time.

Now that the Athenians had become highly civilized, they were interested in education. However, women were not given the same rights as men. For this reason a girl in Athens was given little education. She was never sent to school, but was taught only by her mother and her nurse. Usually she learned about housekeeping, how to spin, and how to weave. Sometimes she learned to dance, to read, and to write.

Even during Athens' best days Athenian girls and women were kept close at home. Of course, they were not allowed to take part in the government.

The Athenian boy, however, was given an education. During his first seven years he also was taught at home by his mother and his nurse. There he learned the stories of the Greek gods and heroes and how to sing. But most of his time was given over to playing games in the bright sunshine.

If an Athenian boy came from a wealthy family, he spent most of his time with a slave, who was called a pedagogue. These pedagogues were usually bright, well-educated young men who had been captured during some war between their own country and Athens.

It was the pedagogue's duty to carry his pupil's lunch, books, writing materials, and musical instrument. In fact, the pedagogue looked after the boy both in and out of school. He also taught the boy to walk, sit, and stand gracefully and to have good manners.

At the age of seven the Athenian boy's education at school began. The school he attended was not like ours of today. It was held in the teacher's house or even out in his yard. If a pupil disobeyed he was severely punished.

In these schools, which were attended by only a few boys, the pupils were taught music, reading, and writing. In these days every boy was expected to be able to sing the battle songs of his people and the songs about the Greek heroes. He was also expected to play at least one musical instrument. Usually he played the harp, the lute, or the lyre. Music was taught in order to train the boys to love beautiful things. Athenian boys also learned the poems of Homer and of the other great Greek poets. Thus they learned to love and to honor the Greek heroes.

Among the other subjects learned were a little arithmetic, some geography, and some history. But these subjects were little taught. The Athenians felt that a boy could better spend his time in studying beautiful things than in studying subjects that were merely useful.

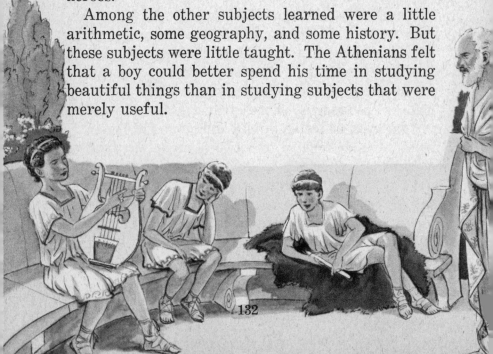

Reading, writing, and drawing were also studied in these ancient Athenian schools. Most Greek pupils wrote on tablets made of wood and covered with wax. A sharp-pointed tool, or stylus, was used to scratch the letters onto the soft wax.

Games and Sports in Athens

The Greeks thought that physical training was even more important than any of the other subjects which they were taught. This bodily training was given in a school called a gymnasium. Here the boys learned to play games, to take part in many sports, and to exercise every day. They were taught to dance, swim, run, jump, wrestle, box, and ride. Every boy was also taught to throw the spear and to use the bow.

Because the Greeks admired their gods, they wanted to be like them. For this reason they tried to have strong, graceful, and beautiful bodies. For this reason, too, they were willing to spend a great deal of time in training their bodies. The boys who were the strongest and the most graceful took part in the games and sports held in honor of the gods.

At the age of eighteen an Athenian boy went into a camp where he was trained to be a soldier. After he had spent a year there, he was placed as a guard in some lonely spot and given the hardest sort of training. The aim was to harden him and to make a brave soldier of him. After being a soldier for two years, the young Athenian became a citizen and was allowed to vote.

Of all the celebrations held in honor of the gods, the Olympic Games were the most famous. They were held at Olympia every four years in honor of Zeus. Greeks from all parts of the country and even from many of the Greek colonies came to this celebration, which lasted nearly a week.

Those who took part in the games usually went to Olympia and trained for many months. Then when the games took place, people came from far and near to see them. Even though war happened to be going on at the time, all fighting stopped for a month so that people could travel safely to Olympia and to the games.

At first the contests were in running only. Later, wrestling, spear-throwing, and jumping were added. Still later, boxing, horse racing, and chariot racing became exciting contests. Finally even poets, artists, and orators took part in the program which was no longer just for athletes.

The winning of a prize in an Olympic contest was the highest honor a Greek could get. Although the prize was only a wreath of wild olive leaves cut from a sacred olive tree, the winner was thought to be favored by the gods.

For this reason great honor was paid not only to the winner but also to his family. He was given a home and food during the rest of his life. He was also given a special seat of honor at all the public games. Poets wrote his praises, and statues were set up in his honor.

—Selected.

Test and Study Exercises

1. All the sentences below are true. Copy the three that tell best what the main thoughts of this story are.

Under the rule of Pericles everyone in Greece was sure of having enough to eat.

Because Pericles loved Athens, he wanted to make it beautiful.

Everyone in Athens was able to go to the theater whenever he liked.

Much talking took place in meetings, called assemblies.

A sharp-pointed tool, or stylus, was used to scratch the letters onto the soft wax.

2. Who was Demosthenes?

3. Who was Plato?

4. What fact about the school boys and girls of old Athens interests you most?

Word Friends

PREPARATORY NOTE: Your friend John wouldn't like it if you called him "Jane." Words are our friends, too, and we should be careful to call them by their right names.

Have you ever thought of words—*spoken* words—as being very much alive? Well, they are! Words speak for us. They carry our thoughts. They show others how we feel. They go with us wherever we go —to school, to parties, to playgrounds, and to the parks. Words go everywhere. Wouldn't our days be dull and uninteresting without them? Can you imagine a party without words?

Words are really our very good friends; yet sometimes they are mistreated, neglected, and ignored. The vowels and consonants of which they are made are often mispronounced, which is the same as calling a word friend by its wrong name!

Are the vowels in the words that you use always correct? The vowels, you know, are the free and open sounds of speech: *a, e, i, o, u.* Do yours always come through your mouth instead of your nose, as well-behaved vowels should? Are they placed well forward, instead of back in your throat? Distinctness of speech depends upon this.

Do you always show the difference between *short i, short e,* and *short a* when you use these words:

pin	pen	pan
tin	ten	tan
mit	met	mat
sit	set	sat

136

Do you hear and sound the difference between *who* and *hue, moo* and *mew, do* and *due, coo* and *cue, booty* and *beauty?* And do you always pronounce *tulip, duty, tune,* and *Tuesday* with the *long u* sound as in *you?* And do you pronounce *room, hoof, roof,* and *root* with the same vowel sound as in *boot?*

Other vowels that are often miscalled are found in these words: *catch, just, instead, radish, because, grass, dance, ask, began, was* and *nobody.*

The *ou-ow* words need watching, too. Do you remember that they are made of two sounds: *ah* and *oo?* The jaws must open wide, and the tone come through the mouth as you say: *brown, down, town, ground, sound, around, mound, bound, mountain, fountain,* and others of that *ou-ow* family.

Test and Study Exercises

1. Should vowel sounds come through the mouth or through the nose?

2. Why are words of such great importance?

3. In what way are the words on each line below supposed to sound different? Read them from left to right.

pin	pen	pan
tin	ten	tan
mit	met	mat
sit	set	sat

The Lady Rain

The Lady Rain has many voices—low, and sweet, and shrill. You may have heard her, laughing in a silver-throated trill at the tiny cowslips frolicking upon the meadow hill.

I know you've seen her trip across the pale green April grass, spilling perfume on the violets that smile to see her pass—her voice a crystal tinkle like the clinking of clear glass.

Have you heard the lady comforting the tired, sleepy stream—murmuring so softly that almost it would seem you can hear her whisper, "Shh. Sleep, stream—dream."

Sometimes she mutters angrily, and thunders to the ground to drown your budding garden, and strew wet leaves around—to a hard and heavy, dreary, weary, teary sort of sound.

But the lady is more often kind, and croons a lullaby to baby birds that waken in the lonely dark, and cry. Her voice is quiet—soft and sweet—a whisper and a sigh.

The Lady Rain has many voices, but one throat to sing them through—to laugh and scold, to cry and croon—as your *own* voices do. When she comes across the shining roofs, what does she say to you?

—*Irene Cameron.*

HISTORY

INDIANS
and
HEROES

Daniel Boone in Trouble

Preparatory Note: As you read this play, try to think how each character should talk, act, and look. Be ready to help your teacher and the class plan to act the play.

Characters

Daniel Boone   Third Pioneer
Simon Kenton   Fourth Pioneer
General Hamilton   A Young Pioneer
Major Bound   Chief Black Fish
Tompkins   Mingo, a Brave
Wilson   First Brave
First Pioneer   Second Brave
Second Pioneer   Third Brave
Pioneers, English Soldiers, Braves

SCENE I

TIME: *January, 1778.*
PLACE: *Blue Lick Springs, Kentucky.*

The pioneers are seen in camp. Over fires hang large kettles. Some of the pioneers stir the boiling water in the kettles; others take salt from the kettles; others carry water from the springs near by.

Kenton. Three pounds of salt I've taken from my kettle!

First Pioneer. I think I can soon take salt from mine!

Second Pioneer. There are signs of it in mine!

Third Pioneer. Two more days will see us through this work, I think.

Fourth Pioneer. And on the road back home, I hope!

First Pioneer. I hope so too, comrade! I fear the Indians will attack the fort while we are here.

A Young Pioneer. Oh, there is no danger of that!

Kenton. There is always danger of that, my boy.

Young Pioneer. Then why did Colonel Boone bring us here, so far away from the fort?

Kenton. Why, it was because we needed salt! You know how we were suffering from the lack of it.

All. Aye! Aye!

First Pioneer. Boone knew we had to take the risk some time.

Second Pioneer. It is strange that Boone does not return from hunting.

142

Third Pioneer. Well, we were out of food and perhaps game has not been plentiful.

Fourth Pioneer. But he went out at daybreak, and it is now past noon. (*He looks at sun.*)

Kenton. Well, he's safe; you can count on that. He knows these forests as we know the Boonesborough fort.

All. Aye! Aye!

(*They continue their work. The* Young Pioneer *goes to the springs for water.*)

Young Pioneer (*looking off; low voice*). Sh! Sh! Indians! They've got Boone!

Pioneers (*getting rifles*). Boone?

Young Pioneer (*nodding*). They're bringing him here! Sh!

Pioneers lift rifles. Enter Boone *with four young Indians.*)

Boone. Put down your rifles, comrades. I am their prisoner.

Kenton. You need not long remain so. (*He aims his rifle at an Indian. The pioneers aim at other Indians.*)

Boone. Don't shoot! We do dare not to touch them! One hundred braves are in the woods about us!

Kenton. They surround us?

Boone. They surround us now on every side! They came upon me suddenly. I ran, but was soon overtaken by these younger Indians, and I surrendered.

First Pioneer. Surrendered? Without a fight?

Boone. Yes; I found they were marching upon Boonesborough.

All. Boonesborough?

Boone. Yes! I thought of the handful of men there to defend the fort. I thought of the women there, and children. I determined to stop their march at any price. I know their custom—to return to camp to show off their prisoners; to exult over them, as children over Christmas toys, and so I surrendered. I am sure they will return at once, if you, too, will surrender.

Second Pioneer. Surrender! Only cowards surrender! We can at least kill some of them!

Pioneers. Aye! Aye!

Boone. Yes, we might kill some of their best warriors. And what would happen then? The Indians would be wild with anger. They would march upon our fort at once and kill all without mercy.

First Pioneer. Only cowards surrender!

Pioneers. Aye! Aye!

Boone. Men, men! Do not think of proving your own bravery at this time! You are all brave men! You are willing to die to save your friends, every one of you!

Pioneers. Aye! Aye!

Boone. But dying will not save them, comrades! You must live to save them. Surrender and the Indians will return to camp, and Boonesborough will be safe.

(*There is a long pause.*)

Kenton. I will surrender!

Second Pioneer. I will surrender!

Other Pioneers. And I! And I! And I!

Boone. Then give your rifles to these Indians. (Boone *motions to Indians, who take rifles.*)

Indians (*joyfully*). Wah! Wah! Wah! (*At once Indians spring in from all sides and surround pioneers.*) Wah! Wah! Wah!

A Brave. Show white men at camp, Chief Black Fish!

Another Brave. All camp happy when see white men, Chief!

Braves. Wah! Wah!

(*Pause; all look at* CHIEF BLACK FISH.)

Chief Black Fish. Take white men to wigwams!

Indians. Wah! Wah! Wah!

(*They go with prisoners.*)

Scene II

TIME: *One month later.*
PLACE: *British fort, Detroit.*

(GENERAL HAMILTON, MAJOR BOUND, *and many English Soldiers are seen.* TOMPKINS, *a soldier, enters and salutes the* GENERAL.)

General. Well, Tompkins?

Tompkins. There's a squad of Indians waiting, General. Chief Black Fish asks to see you, sir. He has prisoners, sir.

General. White men?

Tompkins. Yes, General.

General. Bring them here, Indians and prisoners. (TOMPKINS *salutes and goes.*) Please bring the money, Major, to ransom these white men.

Major Bound. Yes, General. (*He salutes; crosses room and gets a bag of money from a chest.*)

(*Enter* CHIEF BLACK FISH, MINGO, *and other braves, with* BOONE *and pioneers.*)

Chief Black Fish. Prisoners, great Chief—white men—ransom.

General (*taking bag of money*). How much?

Chief Black Fish. One—not sell. He—Daniel Boone!

General. Daniel Boone! Step forward, Boone, I want to know you. (BOONE *steps forward. The* GENERAL *offers his hand.*) I have heard much about you, Colonel; your courage and your justice to enemy as well as friend. (*Lowering his voice.*) I'll ransom you, Colonel Boone.

Boone. I thank you, General.

Major Bound. How do they treat you, Colonel?

Boone. With kindness, Major. They have treated us all well since our capture.

Chief Black Fish. Because—glad to get Boone.

Braves. Wah! Wah! Wah!

A Brave. Boone great warrior!

Another Brave. Boone great hunter!

Third Brave. Boone shoot like Indian!

Chief Black Fish (*giving bow and arrows to Boone*). Show! (*He sticks a feather into a crack of door.*) Show!

(Boone *shoots; hits feather.*)

Indians (*proudly*). Wah! Wah! Wah!

Chief Black Fish. Mingo shoot!

(Mingo *steps forward.* Chief Black Fish *puts another feather in door.* Mingo *shoots and misses.*)

Indians (*angrily*). Hi! Hi!

Mingo. Bad arrow—shoot again! (*He shoots and misses.*)

Indians (*angrily*). Hi! Hi!

Chief Black Fish. Boone shoot!

(Boone *shoots and misses.*)

Boone. I too have missed!

Indians (*joyfully*). Wah! Wah! Wah!

First Pioneer. I have never seen him miss before!

Other Pioneers. Nor I! Nor I!

Second Pioneer. Shoot again, Boone!

Third Pioneer. Show them what a white man can do, Colonel!

Boone. I can do no better than my Indian brothers. I will not shoot again.

147

Indians. Wah! Wah! Wah!

General (*taking money from bag*). Chief Black Fish, here is ransom for the white men.

Chief Black Fish. No sell Boone.

General. Here is money for all but Boone—two hundred dollars. (CHIEF BLACK FISH *takes the money and motions to the braves, who release pioneers.*) Now here are two hundred for Boone alone.

Chief Black Fish. No sell Boone!

General. Three hundred!

Chief Black Fish. No sell Boone!

General. Four hundred!

Chief Black Fish. No.

General. Five hundred!

Chief Black Fish. No.

General. Six hundred!

Chief Black Fish. No sell Boone any money! Boone an Indian! Boone my son! Many moons try to get him—take him to wigwam now!

Indians. Wah! Wah! Wah!

Boone. It is useless, General. I must go back with them, you see.

General. Yes, it is useless. Take my fur coat, Colonel. You will need it on your journey.

Major Bound. Take my fur gloves and leggings, Colonel.

Boone. No, no, gentlemen! I am a poor man. I could never hope to pay you.

General. We do not want pay, Boone.

Boone. I cannot take such gifts. But I thank you, gentlemen, I thank you.

Chief Black Fish. Come, my son.

Boone. Farewell, friends! Farewell comrades! (*He goes with Indians.*)

Scene III

Time: *three months later.*
Place: *the open just in front of Boonesborough fort, which is seen back.*

(*Gates of fort are open. Pioneers are seen outside fort, surrounding* Wilson. *A pioneer runs to fort.*)
Pioneer (*calling*). Wilson has escaped from the Indians. He is here with us outside!
(*Other pioneers and* Kenton *enter from fort running. They shake hands with* Wilson.)
Kenton. Wilson! I feared we would never see you again!
Wilson. I am thankful to get here alive.
Kenton. What news of Boone?
Wilson. Boone is now an Indian.
Kenton. Boone an Indian!
Wilson. He was made a member of the Chief's own family, and all with his consent. He's a traitor to his race, I say!
Kenton. He may have had some reason—
Wilson. There was no reason. I say we should drive him back should he ever come to us again!
Pioneers. Aye! Aye!
First Pioneer. I've noticed he was always kind to Indians where others would be harsh.
Second Pioneer. I've seen that many times, and wondered at it.

149

Kenton. Boone was only just to the Indian. You all know that full well!

Third Pioneer (*looking off*). On guard! An Indian! See him running in the valley there! Shoot him!

Kenton. No, no! He calls to us! Listen!

Indian (*faintly, from a distance*). Boone! Boone! Boone!

Kenton. Do you hear? He calls, "Boone!"

A Pioneer. It's only an Indian trick. Shoot him!

Kenton. No, no! Listen!

Indian (*calling nearer*). Boone! Boone! Boone!

Wilson. Shoot him now, I say!

Kenton. I forbid it! He may bring news of Boone!

Wilson. What is that to us? Boone is a traitor to the white man!

Pioneers. Aye! Aye!

Kenton. Well, come within the fort. We'll soon find whether it is a trick or not. And then we'll shoot in safety. If that Indian is an enemy, we risk our lives by staying here. Come!

Pioneers. Aye! Aye!

(*They enter fort and close gates. Pause.* Boone, *in Indian dress, enters, running.*)

Boone. Open the gates, friends! It is I—Boone! (*Silence; pause.* Boone *tears off his headdress of feathers and throws it on ground.*) Don't you know me? I am Boone—Daniel Boone! (*Silence; pause.*) Men, men, do you shut me out from you? Is that what your silence means? (*Silence; pause.*) Do you think I joined the Indian tribe by choice? Do you think I am a traitor to you and my race? (*Silence; pause.*)

Your silence answers me. Listen, comrades—I took my first chance to escape! One hundred sixty miles in four days I have come; stopped once and only once to eat, and not at all to sleep. And this I have done to warn you—to tell you that Chief Black Fish comes to attack you! With four hundred warriors, he is now upon the march! Now, drive me from you, if you will. Daniel Boone was never traitor to his kind— never was and never will be! But traitor to the Indian he is. To learn their plans, he became an Indian. He tricked them to save his own. Do you hear that, men? It was to save his own.

(*The gates are opened, and the pioneers rush out. They grasp* BOONE'S *hands.*)

Kenton. Boone, Boone, you have saved us! Forgive us!

Pioneers. Forgive us! Forgive us!

Boone. I do forgive, for I know you did not understand. You are all my friends and comrades.

—*Augusta Stevenson.*

151

Test and Study Exercises

1. "Daniel Boone in Trouble," which you have just read, is called a *play*. What would you say are the main differences between a play and a story?

2. What were the pioneers doing when Boone and the Indians came?

3. (a) Why did Boone tell his men not to shoot? (b) What did his men think of that order at first?

4. Why did the Indians like Boone so much?

5. Some of the pioneers thought that Boone had left them to live with the Indians. Which pioneer would not believe that?

Suggested Activities

1. Find one or two other books or stories that tell something about Daniel Boone. Write the names of the books in which you find something about him.

2. With your teacher's help, the class will act out this play. If you have a part, be sure to read it as you think the person in the play would have said it.

How Forked Lightning Became Chief

PREPARATORY NOTE: The Indians liked brave men. They also liked wise men, and there were many wise Indians. Read this story to learn how one tribe of Indians chose their chief.

The Meeting of the Tribe

When the old chief of the Moccasin tribe of Indians died, he left no heir.

"We must now choose a new chief," said the men of the tribe in council.

"Give us an old man!" said Bald Eagle, who long had wished to be chief.

"Give us a young man!" said Red Fox, who had dreamed every night since the old chief died that he had been made leader of the tribe.

"The old man has wisdom with him!" said Bald Eagle; "the young man has to learn it."

"Old age forgets wisdom. Old age hesitates!" said Red Fox, quoting sayings of his tribe. "Youth hopes all things. Youth fears naught. The greatest wisdom is with the bravest."

"Then the greatest wisdom is with Bald Eagle!" said the old man.

"Not greater than with Red Fox!" said the young man.

"Who ever saw Bald Eagle cower in battle?" asked the old man.

"Who ever saw the look of fear on the face of Red Fox?" asked the young man.

"Bald Eagle has sixty scalps hanging in his wigwam!" said the old man.

"And he has been here sixty years. Red Fox has been here only thirty years, and he also has a scalp for every year of his life!" argued the young man.

And then there came a pause.

"Give us Forked Lightning for our chief!" said a voice in the council. " 'Not a braver man have I in battle,' used to say our old chief, when he talked of the deeds of Forked Lightning; 'not a braver or a wiser!' he often said."

"Give us Red Fox!" cried another voice. "He is brave and strong. He is our noblest warrior."

"Give us Forked Lightning!" cried one voice, and then another. "Give us Forked Lightning; and then our old chief in his grave will rule us with his counsel still."

"If we all be equal, then, in valor and in wisdom," said Red Fox, stepping out before the council, "give us him who is our highest leaper, who is our strongest and most active wrestler, who shoots the straightest with the bow and arrow!"

"Have we a higher leaper than Forked Lightning, or a stronger and more active wrestler, or one who shoots straighter with the bow and arrow?" asked a friend of Forked Lightning.

"Perhaps so; perhaps not. We can find out tomorrow!" answered Red Fox.

Then the council was dismissed, and word went throughout the village and other villages that on the morrow Red Fox and Forked Lightning would contest to determine who should be the chieftain of his tribe.

By sunrise a great crowd was in the village from far and near to witness the contest.

"Eat with us beside our wigwams, then smoke with us, and be our guests till the contest is ended," said the men of the village, welcoming the visitors.

And they sat down beside the wigwams and ate, and then they smoked and told tales of their tribes, or guessed as to whether Red Fox or Forked Lightning would win in the contests; and the maidens peeped from the wigwams at the young men who had come to the village.

The council selected a chief of a neighboring tribe to conduct the contests and decide the winner who would become chief.

At the appointed time this big chief moved to a long, broad level by the grove back of the village, followed by all the men and boys. Red Fox and Forked Lightning were in their gayest costumes, and each was surrounded by his friends.

The Contest

When the grove was reached, the people arranged themselves to witness the contests.

"Red Fox and Forked Lightning, stand forth!" demanded the chieftain who was in charge.

Red Fox and Forked Lightning stood forth.

"The one of you who today," began the stern chief, "shall show himself the higher leaper, the stronger and more active wrestler, the more skillful with the bow and arrow, and the swifter runner, or who shall show himself superior in any three of these, that one shall be chieftain of his tribe, unless it should be that one of you should show himself today to be what neither of you has shown himself to be before this time—wiser and braver than the other. He who is the wiser and the braver shall be chieftain, whoever may be swifter, or stronger and more active, or higher in leaping, or more skillful with the bow and arrow."

And all the men wondered why this chief, a man known far and wide for his wisdom, should talk about wisdom and bravery in such contests as these, and thought within themselves that he was not so wise as they had heard. But they said nothing, only thought.

"Come here," said the chief, speaking to Big Cloud and Black Hawk, Indians from other tribes. "Hold this stick on the tips of your fingers, chin-high."

The stick was raised.

"Red Fox," commanded the chief.

Red Fox cleared the stick with a beautiful leap.

"Forked Lightning!"

Forked Lightning rose high above the stick, descending in a graceful curve.

"Eye-high!"

The stick rose eye-high.

"Red Fox!"

Red Fox cleared the stick again.

"Forked Lightning!"

Forked Lightning again rose over the stick.

"Above your heads!" ordered the chief.

Up rose the stick high in the air, and all the Indians rose in anxiety.

"Red Fox!"

In an instant from far back among the trees, like a thing flying in the air, came Red Fox, and like a thing flying in the air he rose and described a beautiful semicircle over the stick.

A great shout went up. "I have never seen a leap so high!" said some.

"Forked Lightning!"

From far back among the trees came Forked Lightning, every nerve strained, and determination in his whole face. High rose he in the air, but the soles of his moccasins touched the stick and it fell rattling to the ground.

"Won by Red Fox!" announced the grim chief; and a mighty shout rose from the friends of the winner.

"We shall now determine who is the better wrestler," said the chief.

"Red Fox is older and heavier than Forked Lightning, and it is not fair that they should wrestle unless they are of the same age and weight!" said the friends

of Forked Lightning, and hotly they argued with the friends of Red Fox; but Forked Lightning took no note of what his friends were saying, and while they were arguing, he stripped himself for the wrestling bout.

Long he and Red Fox wrestled. Red Fox was the stronger, but Forked Lightning was quicker, and often his friends thought he was going to win; but finally Red Fox massed his strength, and with a mighty effort pressed Forked Lightning to the earth.

"Won by Red Fox!" announced the chief, and a loud shout rose again from the friends of the winner.

"We shall now decide who has the more skill with the bow and arrow!" rang out the voice of the chieftain.

"Red Fox is older and has had more practice with the bow and arrow than Forked Lightning, and it is not fair that they should be matched in such a contest!" said the friends of Forked Lightning; and they and the friends of Red Fox disputed long; but Forked Lightning took no note of what his friends were saying, and while they were arguing he came forth with his bow and quiver, saying he was ready for the match.

Far out among the trees on the breast of a mighty oak they placed the target. Straight to the center of the target flew the arrow from the bow of Red Fox.

Straight to the center of the target flew the arrow of Forked Lightning. Straight again to the center of the target flew the arrow from the bow of Red Fox.

Away flew the arrow from the bow of Forked Lightning, but it entered the center at an angle.

"Red Fox has won!" cried the big chieftain; and loud rose the shouts from the friends of the winner. "Red Fox is our chief! Red Fox is our chief!" they shouted, and sent runners to announce it in the village.

"Next is the contest in running," said the chief.

"There is no need of a contest in running!" said the friends of Red Fox. "Red Fox has already won in three contests!"

"Now comes the contest in running," announced the chief, taking no notice of what was said to him.

"There is no need of a contest in running," spoke up Red Fox. "Red Fox has won in three contests, and by the conditions is already chief."

"Red Fox is afraid to run," said the friends of Forked Lightning. "A swifter runner than Forked Lightning has not been born in our tribe."

"Now comes the contest in running!" exclaimed the chief again, not heeding what was said by others.

"Red Fox will not run! Red Fox has already won! Red Fox is already chief!" spoke out Red Fox, in a tone of anger.

"Red Fox is right," said the stern chief. "There is no need of a contest by running."

All the Indians gathered together to hear the chief proclaim Red Fox the winner.

"Whoever should win in all or three of these contests," he began quietly, "should be made chief unless the other should show himself wiser and braver! Red Fox has honestly won in three of the contests, and might have won in the fourth had he not been afraid of defeat. Forked Lightning refused to enter no contest, although in all, unless it was the fourth, he knew the chances were against him. He did the best he could in each contest, willing to risk defeat for the chance of victory. This is true wisdom and bravery. He who is not willing to bear defeat is the greatest of cowards, and has neither the wisdom nor the bravery that should be in the heart of a chieftain. Forked Lightning, therefore, I declare the winner and henceforth the chieftain of his tribe."

Then there was a great silence, for the chief had uttered a new thing, and they were thinking whether he was right. They stood with their heads bowed.

"The big chieftain is right," they began saying presently to each other. "He was right!" they repeated on their way to the village. "The chieftain was right! Forked Lightning should be our chief!"
—*Henry W. Fugate.*

160

Here are eight sentences that tell something about the story you have just read. The sentences are not in the order of the happenings they tell about. Write them in the correct order.

The Indians had to choose a new chief.

Red Fox won the jumping contest.

The Indians decided to have a contest.

Some Indians said they wanted Red Fox as chief, and others said they wanted Forked Lightning.

Red Fox won the wrestling contest.

Red Fox said there was no need of a running contest.

The other Indians agreed that Forked Lightning should be their chief.

Red Fox won the archery contest.

Tribal Roll Call

PREPARATORY NOTE: This poem tells how each tribe might have answered, if the Indians had been assembled and the roll had been called. Read your part clearly and proudly.

Group I: We were the woodsmen of the East;
               We ranged from Maine to Illinois;

Solo 1:   Chippewa . . .
Solo 2:   Seminole . . .
Solo 3:   Cherokee . . .
Solo 4:   Iroquois . . .

Group II: We were the Northwest fishermen
               Who lived by roaring rivers;
                    We speared our fish,
                    Brought down our game
               With arrows, bows, and quivers.

Group III: We were the blanket-weavers,
               The shepherd Navajo.
                    Our flocks grazed
                    On the Southwest plains
               Where sage and cactus grow.

Group IV: We were the huntsmen of the plains,
               Stalking deer and buffalo:

Solo 5:   Cheyenne . . .
Solo 6:   Spokane . . .

Solo 7:   Ponca . . .
Solo 8:   Crow . . .
Solo 9:   Blackfoot . . .
Solo 10:   Ute . . .
Solo 11:   Arapaho . . .

All: Not so many years ago
            We crossed the streams by birch canoe;
            We rode our ponies on the plains:

Solo 12:   Osage . . .
Solo 13:   Omaha . . .
Solo 14:   And Sioux . . .

—Louise Abney.

Test and Study Exercises

1. Which tribes are called the "woodsmen of the East"?

2. Who were the "blanket-weavers"?

3. Who were the "huntsmen of the plains"?

4. Which names of Indian tribes are most interesting to you?

5. Which lines of this poem do you like best to read aloud? Why?

The Boy Who Saved a Regiment

PREPARATORY NOTE: Our great George Washington praised the boy whom you'll meet in this story. Read to find out whether or not the boy deserved the praise which he received.

Who Gets the Powder Horns?

"You are not tall enough to carry a musket! Go with the drums, and play on that fife you blew at the Battle of Saratoga. Away with you, little Jabez, crying for a powder horn, when grown men like me have no place to keep enough powder for a single charge!"

A tall, thin Vermonter, whose uniform was a wool blanket wrapped around him to his knees, laughed loudly from the door of his log hut as he made fun of the soldier lad.

A little way down the snowy street of these rude cabins a group of ragged comrades was crowding at

164

the heels of a man who held a leather apron tightly to his chest with both arms.

Jabez Rockwell was in hot haste to join the chase, but he halted to call back, "It's a lie! I put my fife in my pocket at Saratoga and I fought with a musket as long and ugly as yourself. And a redcoat shot me through the arm. If the camp butcher has powder horns to give away, I deserve one more than a soldier from those new troops without experience. Wait until you are a veteran of the Connecticut line before you laugh at us old soldiers."

The lad stooped to make tighter the thick wrappings of rags which served him for shoes, and hurried on after a small crowd of shouting men which had followed the butcher down to the steep hillside of Valley Forge, where he stood with his back to the cliff.

"There are thirty of you," puffed the fat butcher, "and I have only ten horns, which have been saved from the choicest of all the cattle I've killed these past two months. I wish I had my wooden hammer and skinning knife here to defend myself. Take me to headquarters, if there is no other way to settle this question. I want no pay for the horns. They are my gifts to the troops, but, Heaven help me—who is to decide how to divide them among so many and still please everyone?"

"Stand him on his head and loose the horns from the apron. As they fall, he who finds keeps!" roared one of the party.

"Toss them all in the air and let us fight for them," was another plan.

The unfortunate butcher looked round him with growing fear. At this rate half the American army would soon be around him, thinking they might have a chance to add to their poor equipment.

By this time Jabez Rockwell had turned and twisted through under the arms of the shouting soldiers, until he was close to the red faced butcher.

With ready wit the lad piped up with a plan to settle things, "There are thirty of us, you say, that put you to flight, Mister Ritter. Let us divide the ten horns by lot. Then you can return to your cows with a whole skin and a clean conscience."

"There is more sense in that than in all that has been said by the older soldiers," muttered Master Ritter. "How shall we draw the lots?"

"Away with all this!" cried a sturdy soldier whose long hunting shirt whipped in the bitter wind. "The road up the valley is well beaten down. The old forge is half a mile away. Do you mark a line, and we will run for our lives. The first ten to touch the stone wall will take the ten prizes."

Some agreed, others fiercely opposed, and the argument became louder than before. Master Ritter, who had plucked up heart, began to steal away, hoping to escape in the confusion. A dozen hands seized his collar and leather apron and pulled him back into the argument.

Young Jabez jumped to the top of a huge rock and with the importance of a turkey-cock waved his arms to command attention.

"The guard will be turned out and we shall end this argument by cooling our heels in the prison huts on the hill," he said. "If we run a foot race, who is to say which of us first reaches the forge? Also, those with shoes to their feet have the advantage over those that are bound up in bits of cloth and clumsy patches of hide. Draw lots, I say, before the picket is down upon us!"

The crowd cheered the boy and pulled him from his perch with such friendly thumps that he feared they would break him in two.

Suddenly the noise was hushed. Fur-capped heads turned to face down the winding valley, and without need of an order, the company spread itself along the side of the road in a rude, uneven line. Every man stood at attention, his head up, his shoulders thrown back, hands at his sides. Thus they stood while they watched a little group of horsemen trot toward them.

In front rode a tall commanding figure in buff and blue. The man's stern face, made red and rough by being exposed to all kinds of weather, lighted with a kindly curiosity at sight of this poorly clad crowd, the central figure of which was the butcher, Master Ritter, who had dropped to his knees, as if praying for his life.

General Washington, for it was he, turned to the lively-looking red-haired youth who rode at his side, as if calling his attention to this unusual scene.

The Marquis de Lafayette lifted his shoulders after the French manner and said, laughingly, "It ees vat you t'ink? Vill they make ready to kill 'im? Vat they do?"

The horsemen halted and the soldiers saluted, tongue-tied and embarrassed, and pushing one another in an attempt to urge a comrade to speak up for them, while General Washington gazed down at them as if demanding that someone explain.

The butcher was about to make a stammering attempt when the string of his apron parted and the ten cow-horns were scattered in the snow. He dived after them, and his speech was never made.

Because Jabez Rockwell was too light and slender to resist much, he was first to be pushed forward, and found himself nearest the commander in chief. He made the best of a bad matter, and his frank young face blushed hotly as he took off his old worn cap and bowed low.

"May it please the general, we were in a friendly dispute about those ten cow-horns which the butcher brought among us. There are more muskets than powder horns in our street, and we are debating a fair way to divide them. It is—it is very bold, sir, but dare we ask you to suggest a way out of the trouble?"

A frown clouded the noble face of the chief for a moment and his lips were tight, not with anger but in pain. This scene brought home to him once more that his soldiers, those brave, cheerful, half clothed, freezing followers were without even the simplest tools of war.

Then he smiled, looked down at the straight young lad at his bridle rein and replied, "You have asked my advice as a third party, and it is right that I share in the distribution. Follow me to the nearest hut."

His officers wheeled and rode after him, while the soldiers trailed behind, two and two, down the narrow road, greatly wondering whether reward or punishment were to be their lot.

As for Jabez Rockwell, he walked proudly in advance as guide to the log cabin, and felt his heart flutter as he jumped to the head of the charger, while the general dismounted.

Turning to the embarrassed soldiers, who hung back in the road, Washington called, "Come in, as many of you as can find room!"

The company filled the hut and made room for those behind by climbing into the tiers of bunks filled with boughs to make the rough planks seem softer.

In one corner a slow, smoky wood fire burned in a rough stone fireplace, and made even the general cough and sneeze. He stood behind a bench of barked logs, and took from his pocket a folded paper.

Then he picked up from the hearth a bit of charcoal and said, "I will write down a number between fifteen hundred and two thousand, and the ten that guess nearest this number shall win the ten horns."

He carefully tore the paper into strips and then into small squares, which were passed along to the delighted soldiers.

Over in one corner, jammed against the wall until he could hardly get his breath, Jabez Rockwell said to himself, "I must guess wisely. No doubt he will choose a number midway between fifteen hundred and two thousand. I will write down seventeen hundred and fifty. But, stay! Seventeen seventy-six may come first into his mind, the glorious year when independence of the colonies was declared. But he will surely take it that we, too, are thinking of that number. For that reason I will pass it by."

As if reading his thoughts, a comrade curled up in a bunk at Rockwell's elbow muttered, "Seventeen seventy-six, I haven't a doubt of it!"

Alas for the cunning guess of Jabez, the chief did write down the Independence year, "1776," and when it was read aloud, the boy felt deeply disappointed. This was turned to joy, however, when his guess of "1750" was found to be among the ten nearest that number, and one of the powder horns fell to him.

The soldiers pressed back to make way for General Washington as he went out of the hut, stooping low that his head might escape the roof beams.

Before the party mounted, young Lafayette swung his hat round his head and shouted, "A huzza for ze wise general!"

The soldiers cheered, and General Muhlenberg followed with, "Now a cheer for the Declaration of Independence and for the soldier who wrote down 'Seventeen seventy-six.'"

General Washington bowed in his saddle, and the glad shouting followed him up the valley on his daily tour of inspection.

Jabez Becomes a Hero

In his spare time Jabez scraped and polished the horn, fitted it with a wooden plug and a cord, and with greatest care and labor scratched upon its gleaming surface these words:

Jabez Rockwell, Ridgway, Conn.—His Horn
Made in Camp at Valley Forge

Thin and pale, but still with a brave young spirit, this sixteen-year-old veteran drilled and marched and braved picket duty in zero weather, often without a bit of meat for a week; but he lived through it with no worse damage than various frostbites. In early spring he was assigned to duty as a sentinel of the company which guarded the path that led up the hill to the headquarters of the commander in chief. Here he learned much to make the condition of his comrades seem more hopeless.

Hard-riding scouting parties came into camp with reports of fighting as far as the suburbs of Philadelphia, twenty miles away. Spies, disguised as farmers, returned with stories of visits into the heart of the capital city held by the enemy. The information, which the young sentinel picked up bit by bit, he pieced together to make a picture of a veteran British army, hard to overcome, and waiting to fall upon the "rebels" at Valley Forge. He heard over and over again that the Hessians, with their tall and shining brass hats and fierce mustaches, "were dreadful to look upon," that the British Grenadiers, who tramped the Philadelphia streets in legions, "were like moving ranks of stone wall."

Then Jabez would look out across the valley and perhaps see an American regiment at drill, without uniforms, ranks half-filled, looking like scarecrows. His heart would sink, and in such dark hours he could not believe it possible even for General Washington to win a battle in the coming summer.

It was on a bright day of June that Captain Allan McLane, the leader of scouts, galloped past the huts of the sentinels and shouted as he rode, "The British have marched out of Philadelphia! I have just cut my way through a little fighting over in New Jersey!"

A little later soldiers were buzzing in and out of the old stone house at headquarters like bees, with orders for the troops to be ready to march. As Jabez Rockwell hurried to join his regiment again men were shouting the glad news along the green valley, with songs and cheers and laughter. They fell in as a fighting army, and left behind them the dreadful story of their winter at Valley Forge, as the trailing columns swept beyond the Schuylkill into the wide farm lands of Pennsylvania.

Summer heat now blistered the dusty faces that had been for so long blue and thin with hunger and cold. A week of glad marching and full rations carried Washington's army into New Jersey. The troops knew their chief was leading them to block the British retreat from Philadelphia.

Jabez Rockwell, marching with the Connecticut Brigade, had forgotten his fears of the brass-capped Hessians and the stonewall Grenadiers. One night they camped near Monmouth village, and scouts brought in the news that the British were within sight. In the long summer twilight Jabez climbed a little hill near by and caught sight of the white tents of the Queen's Rangers, hardly beyond musket shot. Before dawn a rattle of firing woke him and he crawled out, to find that the pickets were already exchanging shots.

He picked up his old musket, and chewing a great piece of dry bread for breakfast, joined his company. Knapsacks were piled near Freehold meeting-house, and the troops marched ahead not knowing where they were sent.

Across the field Jabez saw the lines of red which flashed in the early morning sun, and he knew these were British troops. The rattling musket fire became a grinding roar and the deeper note of artillery added to the tumult. A battle had begun, yet the Connecticut Brigade remained in the heat hour after hour restless, troubled, wondering why they had no part to play. As the morning dragged along the men became sullen and weary.

When at last an order came it was not to advance, but to retreat. Falling back, they found themselves near their camping place. Valley Forge had not quenched the faith of Jabez Rockwell in General Washington's power to conquer any odds, but now he felt so troubled that it brought hot tears to his eyes. On both sides of his regiment American troops were streaming to the rear, their columns broken and scattered. It seemed as if the whole army was fleeing from the veterans of Clinton and Cornwallis.

Jabez flung himself into a cornfield and hid his face in his arms. Round him his comrades were muttering their anger and despair. He felt about for his canteen, and his fingers closed round his powder horn, "General Washington did not give you to me to run away with," he whispered; and then his hot, dry lips moved in a little prayer.

"Dear Lord, help us to beat the British this day and give me a chance to empty my powder horn before night. Thou hast been with General Washington and me ever since last year. Please don't desert us now in this time of need."

Nor was he surprised, when he rose, to see the chief riding through the troop lines; but such a chief as he had never known before. The kindly face was now angry and streaked with dust and sweat. The powerful horse he rode was covered with lather, and its heaving sides were marked from hard-driven spurs.

As the commander passed the regiment, his staff at his heels, Jabez heard him shout in a great voice filled with rage and grief, "I cannot believe the army is retreating. I ordered a general advance. Who dared to give an order to retreat? Advance those lines—"

Washington vanished in a moment, with a storm of cheers in his wake. Jabez was content to wait for orders now. He was certain that the Battle of Monmouth would be won by Americans.

His memory of the next few hours was clouded and confused. He knew that the regiment went forward, and then the white smoke of musket fire closed down before him. Now and then the summer breeze cleared the stifling cloud, and he saw it streaked with fire. He aimed his old musket at that other misty line beyond the rail fence whose top was lined with men in coats of red and green and black.

Suddenly his officers began running back and forth, and a shout ran down the thin line, "Stand steady, Connecticut! Save your fire! Aim low! Here comes a charge!"

A moment later Jabez felt his right leg double under him and pain as if red-hot iron had burned it. Then the charging tide of Grenadiers swept over him. He felt the nails in the heels of their heavy shoes bite into his back; then his head felt queer and he closed his eyes. When he found himself trying to rise, he saw, as through a mist, his regiment falling back from their ground after the first shock of the charge. He groaned at the very thought of it. What would General Washington say?

Jabez was now behind the British column, which heeded him not. He was in a little part of the field cleared of fighting, for the moment.

The boy struggled to his feet, with his musket as a crutch, and his wound was forgotten. Alone he stood and reeled, moving his arm toward his broken regiment urging them forward again. The brief calm in the firing made a moment of strange quiet. Therefore the high young voice carried far as he shouted, "Come back, Connecticut! I'm waiting for you!"

His captain heard the boy and waved his sword and shouted to his men. They caught sight of the lonely little figure and his cry went to their hearts. Then a feeling of rage and shame swept the line like a prairie fire and like a wave the men of Connecticut swept forward to capture again the ground they had yielded. Back fell the British before a charge they could not resist, back beyond the rail fence. Nor was there refuge even there, for they were attacked just in the nick of time by the American reserves.

From a low hill to the right of this action General Washington had paused to view the charge just when his line gave way. He sent an officer in hot haste for reserves, and waited for them where he was.

Thus it happened that his eye swept the field from which Jabez Rockwell rose, as one from the dead, to bring his comrades together, alone, without fear. A little later two privates were carrying the wounded lad to the rear. They halted to salute their commander in chief, and laid their burden down as the general drew rein and said, "Take this man to my quarters, and see to it that he has every possible attention. I saw him save a regiment and gain back their position."

The figure being carried on boughs raised itself on an elbow and said very feebly, "I didn't want to see that powder horn disgraced, sir."

With a smile General Washington recognized him and said, "The powder horn? I remember. *You* are the lad who led the powder horn rebellion at Valley Forge. And I wrote down 'Seventeen seventy-six.' You have used it well, my boy. I will not forget."

When Jabez Rockwell was able to join his company again he scratched upon the powder horn this addition to the legend he had carved at Valley Forge:

First Used at Monmouth
June 28, 1778

A hundred years later the grandson of Jabez Rockwell hung the powder horn in the old stone house at Valley Forge which had been General Washington's headquarters. And if you should chance to see it there you will find that the young soldier added one more line to the rough inscription:

Last Used at Yorktown, 1781
—*Ralph D. Paine.*

Test and Study Exercises

1. Copy the sentences below that best tell the main thought in this story.

The butcher was fat.

Everyone wanted to know the best way to divide the cow horns.

General Washington came.

Jabez Rockwell called for the men to come back and fight, and they came.

Washington thought Jabez was a hero.

2. How many horns were there?

3. How did Jabez say the horns should be divided?

4. Who were with General Washington?

5. Be able to tell the meaning, or definition, of each of these words as they are used in the story.

advantage	stern	halted
gazed	musket	noble
comrade	veteran	sentinel
retreat	conqueror	regiment

6. How would you read these sentences aloud?

"I cannot believe the army is retreating. I ordered a general advance. Who dared to give an order to retreat? Advance those lines—"

Suggested Activities

Be able to tell in your own words what this sentence means.

The man's stern face, made red and rough by being exposed to all kinds of weather, lighted with a kindly curiosity at sight of this poorly clad crowd, the central figure of which was the butcher.

An Indian Lullaby

PREPARATORY NOTE: This is a lullaby; so, be sure to read it in a soft, quiet voice.

All: Rock-a-by, rock-a-by, little brown baby,

Solo: Safe in the branches so green and so high,
Shut your black eyes and go to sleep, baby,
     While the wood-wind sings.

All: "Hush-a-by-by."
Alto Voices: "Hush-a-by-hush,"
Solo: 'Tis the voice of the forest.
Soprano Voices: "Hush-a-by-hush,"
Solo: The leaves seem to say.
All (softly):   "Hush-a-by-hush,"
Solo: Sing the wild birds in chorus
Up in the tree-tops so far, far away.

All (softly):   Rock-a-by, rock-a-by, swinging so gently,
See, from the dark woods, so cool and so deep,
The little gray squirrel, the timid brown rabbit,
Are coming to see if papoose is asleep.

179

Solo: Mother will watch by her little
          brown baby,
          Swinging aloft on the green
          branch so high,
          No harm can come to the little
          brown baby,

Alto Voices: Hush-a-by,
Soprano Voices: rock-a-by,
All: hush-a-by-by.

—*Author Unknown.*

Test and Study Exercises

1. What is the purpose of a lullaby?

2. To whom is this lullaby thought to be sung or spoken?

3. What animals are said to be coming to see if the papoose is asleep?

4. Where was the papoose's cradle hung? Why was it hung there?

5. What do the words "wild birds in chorus" mean?

Hiawatha's Canoe

PREPARATORY NOTE: This description of how Hiawatha
made his first canoe is part of a much longer poem. Some
day you may wish to read the whole poem.

"Give me of your bark, O Birch tree!
Of your yellow bark, O Birch tree!
Growing by the rushing river,
Tall and stately in the valley!
I a light canoe will build me,
Build a swift Cheemaun for sailing,
That shall float upon the river,
Like a yellow leaf in autumn.
Like a yellow water lily!

"Lay aside your cloak, O Birch tree!
Lay aside your white-skin wrapper,
For the summer-time is coming,
And the sun is warm in heaven,
And you need no white-skin wrapper!"
Thus aloud cried Hiawatha
In the solitary forest,
When the birds were singing gaily,
In the moon of leaves were singing,
And the Sun, from sleep awaking,
Started up and said, "Behold me!
Gheezis, the great Sun, behold me!"
And the tree with all its branches
Rustled in the breeze of morning,
Saying, with a sigh of patience,
"Take my cloak, O Hiawatha!"
With his knife the tree he girdled;
Just beneath its lowest branches,
Just above the roots, he cut it,
Till the sap came oozing outward;
Down the trunk, from top to bottom,
Sheer he cleft the bark asunder,
With a wooden wedge he raised it,
Stripped it from the trunk unbroken.
"Give me of your boughs, O Cedar!
Of your strong and pliant branches,
My canoe to make more steady,
Make more strong and firm beneath me!"
Through the summit of the cedar
Went a sound, a cry of horror,
Went a murmur of resistance;
But it whispered, bending downward,

"Take my boughs, O Hiawatha!"
Down he hewed the boughs of cedar,
Shaped them straightway to a framework,
Like two bows he formed and shaped them.
Like two bended bows together.
"Give me of your roots, O Tamarack!
Of your fibrous roots, O Larch tree!
My canoe to bind together.
So to bind the ends together,
That the water may not enter,
That the river may not wet me!"
And the larch, with all its fibers,
Shivered in the air of morning,
Touched his forehead with its tassels,
Said, with one long sigh of sorrow,
"Take them all, O Hiawatha!"
From the earth he tore the fibers,
Tore the tough roots of the larch tree,
Closely sewed the bark together,
Bound it closely to the framework.
"Give me of your balm, O Fir tree!
Of your balsam and your resin,
So to close the seams together,
That the water may not enter,
That the river may not wet me!"
And the fir tree, tall and somber,
Sobbed through all its robes of darkness,
Rattled like a shore with pebbles,
Answered wailing, answered weeping,
"Take my balm, O Hiawatha!"
And he took the tears of balsam,
Took the resin of the fir tree,

Smeared therewith each seam and fissure,
Made each crevice safe from water.
"Give me of your quills, O Hedgehog!
I will make a necklace of them,
Make a girdle for my beauty,
And two stars to deck her bosom!"
From a hollow tree the hedgehog
With his sleepy eyes looked at him,
Shot his shining quills, like arrows,
Saying, with a drowsy murmur,
Through the tangle of his whiskers,
"Take my quills, O Hiawatha!"
From the ground the quills he gathered,
All the little shining arrows,
Stained them red and blue and yellow,
With the juice of roots and berries;
Into his canoe he wrought them,
Round its waist a shining girdle,
Round its bows a gleaming necklace,
On its breast two stars resplendent.
Thus the birch canoe was builded
In the valley, by the river,
In the bosom of the forest;
And the forest's life was in it,
All its mystery and magic,
All the lightness of the birch tree,
All the toughness of the cedar,
All the larch's supple sinew;
And it floated on the river
Like a yellow leaf in autumn,
Like a yellow water-lily.

—*Henry Wadsworth Longfellow.*

Test and Study Exercises

1. From what tree did Hiawatha get the bark for use in his canoe?

2. From what tree did he get the boughs to use as braces in his canoe?

3. What did Hiawatha want the quills of the hedgehog for?

Suggested Activities

1. Be ready to tell in your own words exactly what the lines below mean to you.

> Down he hewed the boughs of cedar,
> Shaped them straightway to a framework.
>
> And he took the tears of balsam,
> Took the resin of the fir tree,
> Smeared therewith each seam and fissure,
> Made each crevice safe from water.

2. Find in another book some information about the way Indians made things for themselves, or about canoes. Be able to tell where you found your information, and to tell some of it to the class.

An Old Settler's Story

PREPARATORY NOTE: In this story you will learn about the dangers and hardships of travel in pioneer days.

One bright autumn day, several pioneers were traveling through the wilderness. One of them thus writes of the journey:—

"The driver of our ox team told us to look at the cabin we were passing, as it was the last one we would see for forty miles. That was not a pleasant idea to the younger members of our family. Father and mother seemed to care but little, for they were used to the hardships of the wilderness.

"Slowly we passed along the narrow road. The forest was beautiful with its many bright colors. I was so pleased, that I forgot to watch the sheep that had been left in my care for a short time. Before I was aware of it, every one of them was lost in the woods.

"John and I started out to look for them. I was so anxious to find them that I wandered too far into the woods. I soon saw that I was lost, myself. Horrible

186

thought! I, all alone in the great forest full of wild beasts and Indians!

"I could hear my heart beat, and my eyes became dim. There was no beauty in the woods to me now. I ran and called till I was hoarse, but could hear no answer.

"You, who live near many people, can hardly think how it would seem to be lost in a trackless forest.

"After a few hours, I was found and brought back to the road. We had to leave our sheep to the mercy of the wolves, and proceed on our journey. At night we camped by the side of the road. The rain came down in torrents, and the wind roared in the treetops.

"Next morning the men went out into the woods for the oxen and other cattle. My little brother followed them, but was told to go back to the camp. He started, but went in a wrong direction.

"Just as we were ready to go on, we missed him. How frightened we were, when we knew he was lost! We called and called, till the woods echoed his name for miles around.

"At last we found him, hidden under some underbrush. He had heard us call, but thought we were Indians. So he would not answer or let himself be seen, until he was sure we were friends. We soon started again on our journey. At noon we came to a campfire, which had hardly burned out. It was plain that some other travelers had just passed here.

"They had killed and cooked a deer. Having eaten what they needed, they had turned the other side of it to the fire to cook, thinking perhaps somebody might come that way who would be hungry.

"We were the lucky people who found the dinner in the forest ready cooked for us. How we enjoyed the feast! We wished that we could thank our unknown friends, who had done us this kindness. Perhaps they were as happy in doing it as we were in receiving it.

"As we went on, we soon began to feel the need of water. We searched on both sides of the road for a spring, but none could be found.

"There was no water, except the black puddles in the horse tracks and wagon ruts. I became so very thirsty that at last I shut my eyes and drank from this water in the roads.

"It was not until the next day that we were made happy by reaching a sparkling stream.

"Later we passed an Indian village, which was empty at the time. Many wigwams of poles and bark were to be seen, but the owners had gone off hunting. At the close of another day we reached the end of our journey."

—*Florence Bass.*

Test and Study Exercises

1. Copy the sentences below that best tell the main thought in this story.

Travel in pioneer times was very dangerous.

They passed an Indian village.

It was easy to get lost in the woods.

The Indians had gone off hunting.

Pioneer Songs

PREPARATORY NOTE: These poems tell about wild birds, wild animals, and harvests of grain—all of which were very important to the pioneers in their struggle for food and clothing. As you read the poems try to imagine the sights and sounds which the poet has described.

In the Sky

Solo:	The sky was dark with fanning wings
	As flocks of birds sailed by—
Group I:	White wings,
Group II:	Gray wings,
All:	Black against the sky.
Group I:	Pigeon wings,
Group II:	Hawk wings,
All:	Diving through the air;
Group I:	Eagle wings,
Group II:	Bat wings,
All:	Wings were everywhere.
Solo:	At times the wings blacked out the sun—
	Wild geese were sailing high—
Group I:	White wings,
Group II:	Gray wings,
All:	Black against the sky.

In the Forests

All: The woods were full of game for food—
Wild life was everywhere:

Solo 1:   Raccoons,
Solo 2:   Possums,
Solo 3:   And squirrels in plenty there.

All: In hidden traps which hunters set
The stealthy game were caught:

Solo 4:   Gray fox,
Solo 5:   Red fox,
Solo 6:   And wolves for fur were sought.

All: From these forest trappings
Came furs to keep us warm:

Solo 7:   Fur for mittens,
Solo 8:   Fur for caps,
Solo 9:   For coats against the storm.

All: The woods were full of living things
Hiding everywhere:

Solo 10:   Chipmunks,
Solo 11:   Antelope—

All: All of these were there.

In the Fields

All: Sing a song of plenty,
            The fields are ripe with grain!

Group I: From the seeds
            There came crops;

Group II: From the heavens came the rain.

All: Sing a song of harvest!

Solo 1:   Beneath the summer sun
                Men and women
                Labored daily
            To complete a work begun.

All: Sing a song of feasting!

Solo 2:   Beneath the harvest moon
                There were games
                And there were dances
            To a fiddler's merry tune.

All: From the good earth came the harvest,
            There was plenty, and to spare.
                In the fields
                And streams and forests
            Was abundance—everywhere!

—Louise Abney.

Test and Study Exercises

1. What help did the pioneers get from the sky?

2. In what two ways did the wild animals of the forests help the pioneers?

3. Why were the fields important to the pioneers?

4. What is the meaning of each of the groups of words below as they are used in the poems?

fanning wings	in plenty
hidden traps	stealthy game
forest trappings	labored daily
harvest moon	good earth

5. Choose any two or three lines that go together in one of the poems. Decide how those lines could best be read aloud. Then choose any two or three lines from one of the other pioneer poems, and decide how they could best be read. Be sure to choose lines that should not be read in the *same* way. Be ready to read your lines from different poems aloud.

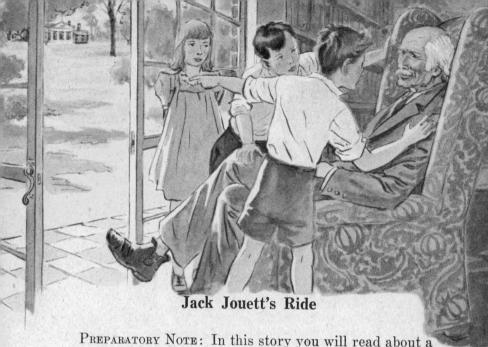

Jack Jouett's Ride

PREPARATORY NOTE: In this story you will read about a man on horseback riding wildly down the street and an enemy army following close behind. It is a thrilling tale, as you will discover when you read it.

The Judge Begins His Story

The judge was sitting in his library, one afternoon, by the window that opened out toward Monticello—Thomas Jefferson's old home. The beautiful view was bathed in the soft light of June. The valley stretching away to the foot of the Little Mountain presented as fair a scene as one often sees,—clear lawns on the high lands, bits of forest, long reaches of hillside, laughing little streams, all lay between the house and the mountains. Everything was quiet, save for the hum of bees or the rattle now and then of a passing train, until suddenly a troop of children dashed in with such a noise that it aroused the judge from his day-dream.

"Oh, papa, papa!" shouted one at the top of his lungs.

"Father, father!" called another.

The judge held up his hand for silence.

"Well, children, what is the matter?"

"We have been playing Paul Revere's ride, and Morris—that's the donkey, you know—has thrown Jack, and now Jack won't be Paul any more, and I want to be one of the citizens, and the others won't ride!" This from a freckle-faced little boy of ten.

The judge checked the speaker.

"Paul Revere's ride? Why don't you play Jack Jouett's ride? That performed as great a service as Paul Revere's ride, and took place right here in your part of the country."

"Why, we never heard of it!" said Jack.

"So much for those who write our histories," replied the judge. "Now sit down, all of you, and be quiet, and I'll tell you all about it."

They were silent at once, and gathered about the judge.

"Your histories tell you of Tarleton, the brave, cruel, English officer. You have heard of his fiery black horse, of his excellent horsemanship, of his cruel legion. Did any of you know that Tarleton once came to Charlottesville with his men? Well, he did, riding right along that road you see crossing the hill in front of the house. He came up here to capture Mr. Jefferson, then the governor of the State, during a meeting of the legislature right here in the old town.

I remember the Eagle Tavern, where the men who made the laws met, and, stranger still, I can remember a person who saw that raid. She was my black nurse's mother, and she died in 1863 when I was ten years old. She was fourteen years old when Tarleton made his raid. Now, how old was she when she died?"

One of the children looked at the judge and smiled. "I know," said she.

"Well?" said the judge.

"Cornwallis came to Virginia first in 1781, so the old woman was ninety-six years old when she died."

"Correct," said the judge. "Her name was Mourning. 'Aunty Mourning,' we always called her,—and my old black nurse used to take me to her cabin, and she would tell me about the 'redcoats' and 'Gin'l' Tarleton and his black horse, and the breakfast he had at Castle Hill.

"In the spring of 1781 the traitor Arnold was at Portsmouth, Virginia, and Sir Henry Clinton sent two thousand men, under General Phillips, to aid him. Soon he and Arnold were at Manchester, a little city just across the James River from Richmond. Cornwallis later invaded Virginia, and met Phillip's command—which had left Manchester without taking Richmond—at Petersburg. They had laid waste the State before them, burning houses, tobacco, and crops, and killing the cattle.

"It looked as if these combined forces would take Richmond this time, so the legislature ended its work to meet again at Charlottesville on the 24th of May. The governor, Mr. Jefferson, came back to his home yonder on the mountain just two miles from us here in Charlottesville, and for a week this town was the capital of the State.

"There were only forty members of the legislature who came to Charlottesville, but among them were men the British would have been delighted to take. There were three signers of the Declaration of Independence: Richard Henry Lee, Thomas Nelson, Jr., and Benjamin Harrison. Patrick Henry, a former governor of Virginia, was there also. He was the man whose clear voice first proclaimed that tyrants should be resisted in the colonies in that sentence you all have learned: 'Give me liberty or give me death!'

"Everything looked very bad for the Continentals in old Virginia at this time. Lafayette, who was in command, had been compelled to fall back. Baron Steuben had been outwitted by the British general, and had been forced to retreat. Cornwallis had pushed up the North Anna River to Hanover County, and there formed the idea of sending Tarleton to capture Mr. Jefferson and the legislature at Charlottesville.

"Tarleton came up into this section of the country. No doubt he laughed to himself, as he rode onward to Charlottesville, thinking what a splendid thing it would be to bring back, tied, the author of the Declaration of Independence, and to have him tried for high treason, and hanged, or transported to Great Britain.

"And Colonel Tarleton came very near succeeding. But for Jack Jouett there might have been no such President as Thomas Jefferson. Yonder mountain, now the Mecca of all lovers of liberty, would not have

196

had upon it that plain monument with the great but simple words: 'Here was buried Thomas Jefferson, Author of the Declaration of American Independence, of the Virginia Statute for Religious Freedom, and Father of the University of Virginia.' There would not have been the great University of Virginia.

"For nobody knew of or suspected Tarleton's raid. Charlottesville, shut in by the mountains, a quiet, retired, little village,—who would care to send a force against it? So Tarleton came swiftly with his legion, and reached Cuckoo Tavern, in Louisa County, not a day's ride away, early one morning in June.

"Now Jack Jouett happened to be at Cuckoo Tavern that day. He was a citizen of Charlottesville, young, gay, and jolly. He kept the inn and was fond of good living and fine horses.

"Why he was at Cuckoo that day no one knows. But I think it was because Jack owned a farm near there, as his will in our old record-book here shows, and he had come down to visit it. But one thing we do know: Jack had captured a British dragoon the day before, and had stripped him of his uniform, which happened to be light blue, and had put it on; coat, trousers, boots, and helmet with long horsehair plume. All these he had on, having clothed his prisoner in his own plain clothes, and then let him go.

"Jack was in the garden when he heard the tramp of the swiftly moving enemy. Concealing himself in the bushes, he saw the redcoats sweep by, for they made no pause at Cuckoo Tavern, and Jack recognized the handsome officer at the head of the troop. Along the road went the dreaded legion, tramp,

197

tramp, tramp of horseshoes, the sound of sabers and bridlebits. 'Mischief in the wind!' said Jack. 'Where are they bound?' and his heart gave a great leap. 'They're after the governor and the legislature! Whee-ooh!' Not a minute did he stay. When the last soldier was out of sight, Jack rushed to the stable, saddled his fine bay mare,—she was said to have been the best bred and fleetest of foot of any horse in seven counties,—and was off at full gallop.

Jack's Great Ride

"Jack knew every road and path in lower Albemarle and Louisa counties. He shrewdly guessed that Tarleton would follow the highway into the main road that led by the countryseats, the homes of the gentry. Jack knew a shorter route, an old road that was not used which would lead him to the river, thence to Monticello, and then to Charlottesville. It was not a pleasant road to ride or drive, though as interesting a route as one often sees. On either side grew great pine trees here, and large oaks there, while brush filled in the spaces.

"The road had once been a buffalo track and then an Indian trail, then a wagon road for a while. But as no one ever worked it or changed the grade, it rapidly washed into little red valleys which made travel almost impossible. So it had not been tried for many years, and nature had covered up the scars made by the animals and man, and only in a few places could one have known that it had ever been used as a highway. Beard grass grew whenever there was an open space; ferns of a hundred varieties clustered in every hollow where water ran; and the wild bramble ran over everything in the shade.

"Into this old road went Jack and his horse, dashing at full speed over hill and valley. It was a dangerous ride, even at a slow gait. The small deep valleys lay concealed under a cover of wild flowers. Ground hog holes were likely to break the leg of his horse. The limbs overhead hit his face, and the wild brier caught him as he passed. His face bore for many years the scars left on his face by this brier, which, you know, climbs up trees and seems to throw itself from one to another.

"But Jack had no time to consider these things. He knew that in a few hours the enemy would be in Charlottesville, and make the governor and legislature prisoners, unless he could give them timely warning. His mare was sure of foot, sound of wind, and no other fox-hunter ever got the brush (or tail) when Jack and she were in the hunt.

"So away he went, touching her lightly with the spur now and then, but oftener cheering her in the race with a merry whistle or encouraging word. He had thirty miles to make. He could have made fifty as easily on a good road as thirty through this wilderness. At one point the road entered a field in sight of the highway along which Tarleton's legion was passing. A few stragglers saw Jack when he dashed into the open.

"They followed him with loud shouts and a pistol-shot or two but when he dashed into the woods they gave up the chase. Once his bay mare fell, her foot having caught in a mass of brier and brush and half-rotten logs; but up she scrambled, and away she went, as if she knew that the fate of the people depended upon her. In two hours Jack rode his thirty miles, and paused in the shallow stream, just opposite the little village of Milton, two miles from Monticello.

"Only a mouthful of water did he allow his gallant bay to sip, and then he dashed up the riverbank and on through the streets of the village, stopping not at anxious hails of men and women, but merely shouting; 'The British are coming! The British are coming!' In ten minutes he drew rein in front of a quaint brick house on top of the now famous mountain. 'He was a sight, too,' the darkies said.

"His face was torn and bleeding from the wild-brier thorns, his gay blue suit covered with mud and dirt, his mare covered with sweat and foam and panting as if her heart would burst through her sides. Down from the porch in front of which Jack

200

had halted came a tall, thin man, dressed in a suit of yellow brown with lace at his wrists and shirt-front, and with a little sword-cane in his hand.

"This man had clear, sparkling blue eyes; a thin skin under which the blood almost seemed starting. His hair was thin and curly, and covered with white powder. For a moment he did not recognize the rider. Then as he drew nearer, 'Why, Mr. Jouett,' he said, 'what brings you here, and with your good horse almost spent?'

"Jack could only gasp, 'The British, governor! Tarleton and his men passed Cuckoo Tavern at six o'clock this morning. Get you gone at once, governor; there's no time to lose. I'll ride to Charlottesville and tell Mr. Patrick Henry and the other legislators.'

" 'But Mr. Jouett,' said Mr. Jefferson, 'have you ridden from Cuckoo since six o'clock? Why, it is not quite eight yet!'

" 'Indeed, but I have, governor; and Tarleton and his men have ridden fast, too, and will be here ere noon—ay, and sooner, too.'

" 'What a debt of gratitude we all owe you, Mr. Jouett!' said the governor. 'One we shall not soon forget. But now, sir; let your gallant bay be rubbed down and fed, and come you to breakfast. We shall have time to send a messenger later.'

" 'Not so governor,' replied Jack. 'I must warn the others.'

" 'True, quite true,' said Mr. Jefferson.

"Jack, in a moment more, again put spurs to his horse. He reached Charlottesville a quarter of an hour later, and soon from house to house ran the

201

news that the dreaded Tarleton was on his way. The legislature met and passed a hurried resolution to adjourn to Staunton, forty miles away, across the Blue Ridge; and the ink was hardly dry on the minute book before Tarleton's advance guard was seen on the crest of the hill not more than a mile away.

"Seven tardy legislators were captured, but, thanks to Jack, one of the most prominent of them escaped. General Stevens, who had been badly wounded at the battle of Guilford Court House, was then boarding at Jouett's Tavern. He was a member of the legislature. After eating a hurried breakfast, and seeing his mare well cared for, Jack mounted another horse, and, in company with General Stevens, who rode a very shabby horse, started off up the Staunton road. They were but a few miles out of town when behind them came rapid horsemen, and they soon saw the red coats of the British troopers.

" 'Jog on slowly, General,' said Jack; 'I'll lead them a dance," and off he dashed. He wore his captured uniform, and the horsehair plume of his helmet streamed out behind him.

"The soldiers thought Jack a general at least, and dashed by the plain old Virginia farmer (as they thought) on the poor, old horse. Jack trifled with his pursuers awhile, now reining up as if about to surrender, now dashing off in a gallop. At last, when he had them well away from General Stevens, who turned into a bypath, he gave spur to his fleet horse, and was very soon beyond the reach of his pursuers. He always said that he never grew tired until he reached the top of the Blue Ridge Mountains, about dark of that eventful day.

"Jack lived and died in Charlottesville. His name is but a faint memory there now, as all of his children moved away. One son, John, went to Kentucky, and was, I believe, the ancestor of a gallant admiral in the United States navy, but there are no Jouetts left in Charlottesville or Albermarle.

"The legislature gave Jack a handsome sword, which young John took to Kentucky with him; but Jack never seemed to think much of his ride, and used to laugh when his neighbors in his old age would talk about it.

"When he died, in 1805, there was talk of a monument to be placed over his grave, and in an old yellow newspaper I have in the library there is mention of a public meeting as late as 1826, called for the purpose of raising money to 'mark the grave of the hero Jouett, and thus save it from being entirely forgotten.' But nothing ever came of it, and now the very spot is unknown.

"Peace be to his ashes! Think of him sometimes, children, and honor his memory."

—*R. T. W. Duke Jr.*

Test and Study Exercises

1. What was the purpose of Jack Jouett's ride?

2. Did Jack do what he started out to do?

3. Is Jack Jouett famous?

4. What is the name of the great man whose old home could be seen from the judge's house?

5. In what state did the happenings of this story take place?

6. Find and write the meaning of each of these words as they are used in this story.

aroused	citizens	governor
legislature	tyrants	recognized
brier	stragglers	opposite

Suggested Activity

Be able to tell in your own words just what the meaning of each of these sentences is.

"So away he went, touching her lightly with the spur now and then, but oftener cheering her in the race with a merry whistle or encouraging word."

"Seven tardy legislators were captured, but, thanks to Jack, one of the most prominent of them escaped."

"Jack trifled with his pursuers awhile, now reining up as if about to surrender, now dashing off in a gallop."

Pocahontas

PREPARATORY NOTE: With Indian enemies all around, and food running low, the settlers needed a friend. Read this story to learn of the Indian girl who saved them.

The Little Indian Tomboy

Many years ago our whole country was a great wilderness. The mountains were covered with forests, and great rivers flowed through miles of territory without a town or city upon their banks. Here and there an Indian village appeared, but as yet no white men were here.

Near one of the great rivers there lived, three hundred years ago, a tribe of Indians called Powhatans. They were ruled by a powerful chief called the Powhatan. He was king over a number of smaller tribes, and was feared and obeyed by all other Indians in the region.

205

The Powhatan who ruled at the time I am going to tell you about was a rather old man. He had thirty-one children, but one little daughter was his special pet and pride. She was brought up like other Indian maidens, trained to be strong, active, and skillful about the work which women did. But this little girl was very fond of running and climbing. She became so swift and light of foot, she was so quick and could do so many things which usually only boys did, that she earned for herself the name Pocahontas, which means little tomboy.

Pocahontas was not only very strong and active in body, she had also a remarkably keen and intelligent mind, like her father, the great chief. She loved all those who were good to her, as we shall see, and she never was afraid to do anything to help a friend.

When little Pocahontas was about thirteen years old, a very exciting thing happened. A party of Indians came to the Powhatan's camp bringing a wonderful white prisoner with them. Pocahontas had heard of the white people who had built themselves strange log wigwams at the mouth of the river, but she had never seen one before. This man was named Captain John Smith, and, like most men who have a great deal of influence over grown-up people, he was very fond of children.

"Who is this little maid with the white feather in her hair?" he asked, as the children flocked about him soon after his arrival.

"Oh, this is Pocahontas," said one of the children in reply. "She wears the white feather because she is a daughter of the chief."

"Then, Pocahontas," said Captain Smith, drawing his knife from his pocket, "come and sit beside me while we see what pretty things I can whittle for you with this." Soon he was the center of a bright-eyed flock of children, making for them many sorts of toys.

Pocahontas was especially pleased with the toys he fashioned for her, and her quick mind found many questions to ask him about his people and their ways, which were strange to her.

Finally the warriors met to decide what to do about Captain Smith. They hardly knew what to do with him. Some of them were afraid of a man who could do so many things they could not understand. They did not understand about his gun, nor the cannon at the white men's new settlement at Jamestown. They did not know about his sword, nor his strange way of building houses. Most of all, they were afraid of a man who could write upon paper so it would tell things to other men who received it many miles away. So they decided to put him to death.

They brought him out before the assembled tribe, forced him to lie down with his head upon two stones, and were all ready to kill him. But just at that moment Pocahontas darted forward, and crying out to her stern old father, she threw her arms about her kind white friend. Powhatan could not refuse the request of his favorite child. Moreover, any Indian had a right to claim the life of a prisoner.

So Captain Smith was allowed to live, and two or three days later he was sent back in safety with four Indians to guide him.

After this Pocahontas went many times to Jamestown to see her white friend.

She soon found that the white strangers were often in need of food. They had not begun to raise crops those first years, and so were not provided with enough food for the winter.

"Come," said Pocahontas to some of her Indian friends one day, "I wish to visit the palefaces again. But they need corn. Let us carry them all we can."

So they gathered up some baskets and filled them with corn which they carried through the forest and down the river to Jamestown.

"Oh, dear and blessed Pocahontas!" cried the white people as they met her coming up from the canoes with her gift, "you have saved us from starving!" and they welcomed her into the town with thankful hearts. Many times after this she came to them bringing food.

Captain Smith bought all he could from the Powhatan and his Indians, but he could not make them sell him enough, so if it had not been for the kindness and help of his loyal young friend, the newcomers would have suffered a great deal more than they did.

Every few months ships from England came to Jamestown bringing new settlers so that the Indians began to be anxious.

"There are too many palefaces," said one. "At first they were only as many as the leaves in winter. Now they are like the leaves in summer."

"We must get for ourselves some of their sticks that kill; then we can fight them," said another. So they bought for corn all the guns and powder they could. At other times some of them stole firearms and tools.

Once when Captain Smith and a little party of his men had been buying corn from the Indians, their boat, loaded with food, was left stranded by the tide. All they could do was to stay all night where they were and wait for the next high tide.

They retired into a rude hut and sent to the Powhatan for some supper.

Meanwhile Pocahontas, in her father's wigwam, heard a plot to surprise and kill the white men.

It was a very cold winter night. There had been snow and everything was frozen; but neither the cold nor the darkness could keep the girl from warning her friend.

Fortunately the little tomboy knew the forest trails well, and was fleet and silent. She reached the white men's hut before the Indians arrived, and rushed in upon her friends.

"Fly!" she cried in great fear. "You must fly at once. My father's men are coming tonight to bring you food, and when you lay down your guns to eat they will kill you."

"We will not lay down our guns, then," the great Captain answered. "Thanks to you, my brave child, we shall be ready and need not fly."

They tried to make her presents of beads and other gay ornaments; but with tears raining down her cheeks, the girl put them aside.

"I dare not have them," she said, "lest the Great Chief know that I have been here. If he know it, I am but dead," and she glided swiftly away through the dark shadows.

It was hardly an hour before the men came from Powhatan with food. But the white men kept their arms beside them and sent a bold message of defiance to the chief. So the red men went back and put off their attack till a more favorable time.

Pocahontas Becomes Lady Rebecca

As the years went on, the distrust and fear between the English and the Indians grew. The white men were not always fair in dealing with the savages and they could do many wonderful things which made the Indians afraid of them and wish to drive them away. Many white men were taken prisoners, though Pocahontas managed to save and send back some of them.

One day Captain Smith was hurt in an accident and had to go back to England.

After this the settlers had more trouble than ever with the Indians. They were not wise and just in dealing with their red neighbors, and at last even Pocahontas kept away from them.

One day, however, the new commander, Captain Argall, found that she was staying with the Potomac Indians, where he was trading. He thought it would be an excellent thing for the English if he could capture her. He offered to give a fine copper kettle to the chief of the Potomacs if he would help.

Accordingly Pocahontas, now a tall and graceful girl of nineteen, was invited aboard Argall's ship. There her Indian friends left her, and she was carried to Jamestown, a prisoner.

Captain Argall at once sent word to the Great Chief that his daughter would be held captive until all the English prisoners and stolen goods were sent back to the town. The Powhatan was much distressed, and sent back a few white prisoners. He could not make up his mind to return all. Yet Pocahontas was still the darling of his heart and he begged the palefaces to be kind to her.

A year passed and Pocahontas was still at Jamestown. The town people were all kind to her, and she was really glad to learn all the things they could teach her. At last one English gentleman grew to love her so much he wanted her to be his wife. His name was John Rolfe. Pocahontas consented, but she asked first to send word to her father.

When the messenger returned he brought the Powhatan's permission, and the chief's brother and two of his sons came to Jamestown to attend the wedding.

Pocahontas took the Christian name Rebecca before she was married, and then the wedding was celebrated just like other weddings of the time.

The Indian chief was proud to have his daughter marry a white gentleman, and from that day there was peace between the two races as long as the Powhatan lived.

About two years after their marriage John Rolfe took his young Indian wife to visit England.

Pocahontas immediately became a very popular person in London. She was presented at court and everybody treated her like a princess and entertained her in a great many ways.

This was partly due to the fact that her old friend, John Smith, was in London, and wrote the queen telling her all about his little Indian friend. So the queen made much of her and it became the fashion for everyone else to do the same.

She was invited to parties and dinners and the theater, and everybody watched her with great interest.

One day Captain Smith called upon her. She was delighted to see him, but when he called her "Lady Rebecca" as everyone else did, Pocahontas covered her face with her hand and turned away for a moment. She could not bear to have him call her anything but his child, as he had done in the American forests. When he understood this he did not address her again as Lady Rebecca, and she happily called him Father, as of old.

At last, however, it came time to think of going back to Jamestown. Pocahontas and John Rolfe with their baby son, Thomas, were making ready to sail when she was suddenly taken ill and died.

Her life had been short, but the little Indian tomboy with her bright mind and loving heart had done a great deal to help in the founding of this country. She had prevented many cruelties. She had saved many people from starving. She had brought about some years of peace, and her little son grew up to have children and grandchildren of his own, who were proud to think that they were descended from "the dear and blessed Pocahontas."

—*Mabel W. S. Call.*

Test and Study Exercises

1. Which one of these sentences tells best what the main thought of the story is?

Pocahontas was a princess.
Pocahontas saved the white men.
Pocahontas married John Rolfe.

2. Copy the sentences below that are true.

Pocahontas wore a white feather to show that she was the daughter of a chief.

The white men were not always fair in dealing with the savages.

The Indians always liked the white men.

Pocahontas went to England.

3. Who was the Powhatan?

4. Who was Rebecca?

Suggested Activities

1. In a reference book or history book find out more facts about Captain John Smith or Jamestown. Be ready to tell the class the name of the book you found, and a few of the facts you found.

2. Be able to express the meaning of this sentence in your own words.

Yet Pocahontas was still the darling of his heart and he begged the palefaces to be kind to her.

NATURE

BIRDS and ANIMALS

The Good Little Cranes Who Were Bad

PREPARATORY NOTE: Cranes are funny looking birds—just feathered bodies walking on stilts. The things they do in this story are funny too, as you will see.

A Home of Their Own

When the Sand-Hill Cranes were married, they began to work for a home of their own. To be sure, they had chosen a place for it beforehand, yet there were other things to think about. Some of their friends told them it would be very foolish to build on the ground.

"There are so many accidents to ground nests," these friends said. "There are Snakes, you know, and Rats, and a great many other people whom you would not want to have look in on your children. Then too, something might fall on the nest."

The young couple talked this all over and decided to build in a tree. "We are not afraid of Snakes and Rats," they said, "but we would fear something falling on the nest." They were talking to quite an old Crane when they said this.

"Do you mean to build in a tree?" said he. "My dear young friends, don't do that. Just think, a high wind might blow the nest down and spoil everything. Do whatever you wish, but don't build in a tree." Then he flew away.

"Dear me!" exclaimed young Mrs. Crane, "one tells me to do this and never to do that. Another tells me to do that and never to do this. I shall just please myself since I cannot please my friends."

"And which place do you choose?" asked her husband, who always liked whatever she did.

"I shall build on the ground," she said decidedly. "If the tree falls, it may hit the nest and it may not, but if we build in the tree and it falls, we are sure to hit the ground."

"How wise you are!" exclaimed her husband. "I believe people get the habit of building just so, and come to think that no other way can be right." And this showed that Mr. Sand-Hill Crane was also wise.

Both worked on the nest, bringing roots and dried grasses with which to build it up. Sometimes they went to dance with their friends, and when they did they bowed most of the time to each other. They did not really care very much about going, because they were so interested in the nest. This they had to build quite high from the ground, on account of their long legs.

"If I were a Duck," said Mrs. Sand-Hill Crane, "it would be very well for me to sit on the nest, but with my legs! Never! I would as soon sit on two bare branches as to have them doubled under me." So she tried the nest until it was just as high as her legs were long.

When it was high enough, she laid in it two gray eggs with brown spots. After that she did no more dancing, but stood with a leg on either side of the nest, and her soft body just over the eggs to keep them warm. It was very tiresome work, and sometimes Mr. Crane covered the eggs while she went fishing. The Cranes are always very kind to their wives.

This, you know, was the first time that either had had a nest, and it was all new and wonderful to them. They thought that there never had been such a beautiful home. They often stood on the ground beside it, and poked it this way and that way with their bills, and said to each other, "Just look at this fine root that I wove in," or "Have you noticed how well that tuft of dried grass looks where I put it?" As it came near the time for their eggs to hatch, they could hardly bear to be away long enough to find food.

One day young Mr. Sand-Hill Crane came home much excited. "Our neighbors, the Cranes who live across the pond," said he, "had two children hatched this morning."

"Oh, how glad I am!" cried his wife. "How glad I am! Those eggs were laid just before ours, so ours must hatch very soon now."

"That is what I thought," said he. "I feel so sorry for them, though, for I saw their children, and they are dreadfully homely,—not at all like their parents, who are quite good-looking."

"I must see them myself," said his wife, "and if you will cover the eggs while I go for food, I will just peep in on them. I will hurry back." She flew straight across the pond, which was not very wide, and asked to see the neighbor's babies. She had never seen any Crane children, you know, since she herself was little. She thought them very ugly to look at, and wondered how their mother could seem bright and cheerful with two such disappointing children. She said all the polite things that she honestly could, then got something to eat, and flew home.

"They are very, very homely," she said to her husband, "and I think it queer. All their older children are good-looking."

She had hardly said this when she heard a faint tapping sound in the nest. She looked, and there was the tip of a tiny beak showing through the shell of one egg. She stood on one side of the nest, watching, and her husband stood on the other while their oldest child slowly made his way out. They dared not help for fear of hurting him, and besides, all the other Cranes had told them that they must not.

"Oh, look!" cried the young mother. "What a dear little bill!"

"Ah!" said the young father. "Did you ever see such a neck?"

"Look at those legs," cried she. "What a beautiful child he is!"

"He looks just like you," said the father, "and I am glad of it."

"Ah, no," said she. "He is exactly like you." And she began to clear away the broken eggshell.

Soon the other Crane baby poked her bill out, and again the young parents stood around and admired their child. They could not decide which was the handsomer, but they were sure that both were remarkable babies. They felt more sorry than ever for their neighbors across the pond, who had such homely children. They took turns in covering their own damp little Cranes, and were very, very happy.

Before this, it had been easy to get what food they wanted, for there had been two to work for two. Now there were two to work for four, and that made it much harder. There was no time for dancing, and both father and mother worked steadily, yet they were happier than ever, and neither would have gone back to the careless old days for all the food in the pond or all the dances on the beach.

The little Cranes grew finely. They changed their down for pinfeathers, and then these grew into fine brownish gray feathers, like those which their parents wore. They were good children, too, and very well brought up. They ate whatever food was given to them, and never found fault with it. When they left the nest for the first time, they fluttered and tumbled and had trouble in learning to walk. A Mud Turtle Father who was near, told them that this was because their legs were too long and too few.

"Well," said the brother, as he picked himself up and tried to stand on one leg while he drew the other foot out of the tangled grass, "they may be too long, but I'm sure there are enough of them. When I'm thinking about one, I never can tell what the other will do."

Still, it was not long before they could walk and wade and even fly. Then they met the other pond people, and learned the names of some of the fish. They did not have many playmates. The saucy little Kingfishers sat on branches over their heads, the Wild Ducks waddled or swam under their very bills, the Fish Hawks floated in the air above them, and the Gulls screamed hoarsely to them as they circled over the pond, yet none of them were long-legged and stately. The things that the other birds enjoyed most, they could not do, and sometimes they did not like it very well.

One night they were talking about the Gulls, when they should have been asleep, and their father told them to tuck their heads right under their wings and not let him hear another word from them. They did tuck their heads under their wings, but they peeped out between the feathers, and when they were sure their father and mother were asleep, they walked softly away and planned to do some mischief.

"I'm tired of being good," said the brother. "The Gulls never are good. They scream, and snatch, and contradict and have lots of fun. Let's be bad just for fun."

"All right," said his sister. "What shall we do?"

"That's the trouble," said he. "I can't think of anything bad that I really care for."

Each stood on one leg and thought for a while. "We might run away," said she.

"Where would we go?" he asked.

"We might go to the meadow," she said. So they started off in the moonlight and went to the meadow, but all the people there were asleep, except the Tree Frog, and he scrambled out of the way as soon as he saw them coming, because he thought they might want him for a late supper.

"This isn't any fun!" said the brother. "Let's go to the forest."

They went to the forest, and saw the Bats flitting in and out among the trees, and the Bats flew close to the Cranes and scared them. The Great Horned Owl stood on a branch near them, and stared at them with his big round eyes, and said, "Who? Who? Waugh-ho-oo!"

Then the brother and sister stood closer together and said, "If you please, we are the Crane children."

But the Great Horned Owl kept on staring at them and saying "Who? Who? Waugh-ho-oo!" until they were sure he was deaf, and answered louder and louder still.

The Screech Owls came also, and looked at them, and bent their bodies over as if they were laughing, and nodded their heads, and shook themselves. Then the Crane children were sure that they were being made fun of, so they stalked away very stiffly, and when they were out of sight of the Owls, they flew over toward the farmhouse. They were not having any fun at all yet, but they meant to keep on trying, for what was the good of trying to be bad if they didn't have fun.

They passed Horses and Cows asleep in the fields, and saw the Brown Hog lying in the pen with a great many little Brown Pigs and one White Pig sleeping beside her. Nobody was awake except Collie, the Shepherd Dog, who was sitting in the farmyard with his nose in the air, barking at the moon.

"Go away!" he said to the Crane children, who were walking around the yard. "Go away! I must bark at the moon, and I don't want anybody around." They did not start quite soon enough to please him, so he dashed at them, and ran around them and barked at them, instead of at the moon, until they were glad enough to fly straight home to the place where their father and mother were sleeping with their heads under their wings.

"Are you going to tell them?" asked the brother.

"I don't know," answered the sister. When morning came, they looked tired, and their father and mother seemed so worried about them that they told the whole story.

"We didn't care so very much about what we did," they said, "but we thought it would be fun to be bad."

The father and mother looked at each other in a very knowing way. "A great many people think that," said the mother gently, "but they find it is a mistake. It is really more fun to be good."

"Well, I wish the Gulls wouldn't scream 'Goody-goody' at us," said the brother.

"What difference does that make?" asked his father. "Why should a Crane care what a Gull says?"

"Why, I—I don't know," stammered the brother. "I guess it doesn't make any difference after all."

The next day when the Crane children were standing in the edge of the pond, a pair of young Gulls flew down near them and screamed out, "Goody-goody!"

Then the Crane brother and sister lifted their heads and necks and opened their bills, and trumpeted back, "Baddy-baddy!"

"There!" they said to each other, "Now we are even."

Clara D. Pierson.

Test and Study Exercises

1. Where did the cranes decide to build their nest?

2. Why do you suppose Mrs. Crane asked Mr. Crane to cover the eggs while she went out to find food?

3. Why did the good little cranes decide to be bad?

4. What birds and animals did the crane children see on their journey?

Suggested Activity

If you have ever seen birds sitting on their nests or feeding their babies, be able to tell the class about it. Remember to use your experience whenever possible to help you understand what you read.

The Sand-Hill Crane

PREPARATORY NOTE: In this poem you will find what some of the other wild things think of the sand-hill cranes.

Whenever the days are cool and clear
The sand-hill crane goes walking
Across the field by the flashing weir
Slowly, solemnly stalking.
The little frogs in the tules hear
And jump for their lives when he comes near,
The minnows scuttle away in fear,
When the sand-hill crane goes walking.
The field folk know if he comes that way,
Slowly, solemnly stalking,
There is danger and death in the least delay
When the sand-hill crane goes walking.
The chipmunks stop in the midst of their play,
The gophers hide in their holes away
And hush, oh, hush! the field mice say,
When the sand-hill crane goes walking.

Mary Austin.

Test and Study Exercises

1. Write on your paper, in pairs, all the words that rhyme in this poem.

2. Why do you suppose all the little animals act as the poet says they do when the sand-hill crane goes walking near them?

The Owl That Listened

PREPARATORY NOTE: Your voice often shows what kind of person you are—happy, grouchy, lively, or sad. As you read this little story try to think of ways to improve your voice.

> "A wise old owl
>   Sat in an oak,
>   The more he saw
>   The less he spoke,
>   The less he spoke
>   The more he heard—
> Why can't we all be like that bird?"

Once upon a time, not so long ago, there was just such a wise old owl perched high up on an oak tree limb. During the day he could not see very well, for the sunlight hurt his eyes; nor did he move about; but he could *hear*. And so he listened, and he listened, and he listened, all day long.

Sometimes a happy laughing voice would reach him, and the wise old owl could tell that the one who had that voice was a pleasant, gracious person. "That voice has a smile in it," thought the owl. Sometimes the happy voice came from a boy who was starting

228

out to fly his kite. Sometimes it belonged to a girl who was having fun on roller skates. In the winter it seemed to come from the snowman under the old oak tree, but the owl, because he was a wise old owl, knew that it came from the children!

Occasionally a gruff voice, deep and harsh and all-in-one-tone, reached the limb where the old owl sat listening. He could tell from the voice that the person who was talking was also disagreeable, unpleasant, and gruff. He could tell that he was out of sorts with the world and everybody in it. Grumpy-grumpy-grumpy was the sound of the voice; shuffle-shuffle-shuffle dragged the feet of the one who had the voice. No happiness there!—not for the harsh-voiced person, nor for anyone who heard him.

The wise old owl was happy when the laughter of little children reached his treetop. Their voices were high in pitch more often than not, but there was excitement and adventure in the tones.

"Their voices sound like fairy bells,
Or fairy laughter in green dells," thought the owl.
"Happy and merry, laughing and gay
Are children's voices at their play!"
The old owl didn't need to see them; he could hear. By listening he could tell more than you could ever guess about everyone who passed beneath his old oak tree. He could tell whether they were in good spirits or whether they were bold or whether they were shy. He could almost tell what kind of homes they came from—happy homes or sad ones. All these things the wise old owl could tell simply by listening to their voices.

229

In the early morning, the owl would hear two words —just two—repeated very often as the folks went on their way to work, or school, or play. "The words are always the same," thought the owl, "but they express different feelings. Just listen to those tones:

morn-
'Good   ing!' There was a little melody that time. A happy voice is going by, singing its morning song." And the wise old owl was glad.

" 'Good
morn-
ing.'

That one is cross. No one will want to talk to him today. His gruff voice shows that he is not interested in other people. What a very selfish person he must be," observed the owl.

ing?'
morn-
" 'Good

My, what a timid little voice she has," thought the owl. "Nobody paid any attention to her. And no wonder! She could scarcely be heard."

Oh, there were ever so many ways in which those two words were said. There were singing tones and dull tones, tinkling and heavy ones, timid and bold. The old owl liked more than anything else to listen to the voices and to guess to whom they belonged. What kind of persons had them? Always to himself, and sometimes out loud, the owl was saying, "Who? Who? Who? Who is coming now?"

And so it is at night, when we stop talking long enough to listen to the voices of the night, we can still hear the wise old owl saying. "Who-oo-oo, who-oo-oo, who-oo-oo . . ." Some folks have called him a hoot owl because of the "hoo-oo-oo," but we know better. He is simply playing his listening game underneath the moon and calling "Who-oo-oo? who-oo-oo?" to the voices that pass beneath his tree.

—*Louise Abney.*

Test and Study Exercises

1. In what way did the owl decide what kind of people were passing or playing near him?

2. Why did the owl think nobody would pay any attention to the girl with the little voice?

3. What did the owl say the happy voices of little children sounded like?

4. Practice saying "Good morning" until you can say it in a gay and happy way.

Old Trip

PREPARATORY NOTE: The boy in this story thought his dog was as good a friend as a boy could have. Read the story to see whether you agree with him.

My Best Friend

When I was a boy I had a friend dearer to me than most of my boy and girl playmates.

This friend was a little black and tan terrier whose name was *Trip*. This name was given him to distinguish him from his mother who was named *Tippy*. I did not know Tippy so well because she died when I was very young. But Trip was the boon companion of my boyhood.

Trip was an animal with personality. That is a big word, but you will know what I mean. Trip was different from other dogs. We just said that Old Trip was smart. Smart meant clever and wise and that is just what he was.

In his earlier years Trip was very lively. He had ambition. As a pup he gathered all the rubbers from the front porches of the neighbors after every thaw. These he deposited on our front porch. It was my job to sort the rubbers and take them back to their owners. My father took care of Trip. Sometimes I heard Trip's quick sharp cries long after I had the rubbers all sorted. Sometimes he would join me as I called at the neighbor's with their rubbers. But I never heard him ask anyone to forgive him for his tricks.

At that time we lived in a little town in the Middle West which was not far from an Indian reservation. The Indians were still very much as they had been in the earlier days. They had not yet bought cheap automobiles nor did they wear white men's clothes. They came to town frequently in a light wagon or buckboard. The whole family would be seated in the wagon with their bright blankets wrapped around them. Two little ponies would draw the wagon down our street. The wagon rattled and the dust rose from the dirt road.

Trip dearly loved to hear an Indian wagon approaching. On certain days, it was the joy of his life, but there were days when he wasn't quite sure. Those days were when father was at home, resting after his long "run." Father was a railroad conductor and he worked nights, running the passenger train out to far-off Dakota.

Father was like Trip. He had personality, too. He didn't believe that dogs should bark or run after Indians. And what Father did not believe in, he did something about. He was not a person who would tell either a boy or a dog to do something and then go off and forget about it—not he. Father spent a good deal of his time when at home training Trip, but when Father was away, Trip was a free soul and enjoyed going when and where he pleased.

One day Father was home working in his bare feet out in the back garden. He dearly loved to work in a garden and especially in the morning when the soil was cool, he liked to free his feet from tight shoes. He had gone barefooted when he was a boy and doing so again helped to recall those pleasant days.

Trip had a fine dust bath in the warm sun underneath the bay window on the south side of the house. Here he would enjoy a nap now and then when he couldn't think of anything else to do.

One fine June morning he was taking a rest when he heard an Indian wagon coming down the street. He could tell by the squeak of the axles. Indians seemed to pay no attention to axles. Most of their wagons squeaked.

Trip's hair bristled up and his ears stuck straight up, and then he listened a moment. He knew his duty and off he went, not yet barking but just getting started so that he could bark loud and long at the proper time. But as he ran, out of the tail of his eye he saw Father in the garden.

Trip had forgotten that father was home. Or perhaps he hadn't been told. Here was a puzzle. What to do? From previous experience Trip knew that if he barked once or charged into the road snapping at the Indians' ponies he would have to settle with Father.

At this moment Trip became an actor. He had an inspiration. He hadn't meant to run after Indians at all or even bark the tiniest bark. All he had meant to do was stretch a little. Still, he could not be sure that Father would understand. Therefore, he had to make his intentions clear. He danced up and down a little, snapped at an imaginary bug in the air, and without halting decided instead to take a brisk run around the house back to his dust bath without father knowing about his error in judgment. Very carefully and with the art of a great actor, he slipped around the back of the house and quietly returned to the safety of the dust bath.

However, Trip's manner was not very convincing. Father saw him as he slipped around the house. He noticed a slightly guilty air about the dog.

"Eh, eh," said Father as the dog slid into his haven of safety, "saw me, didn't you?"

At the sound of Father's voice Trip began another act, which he thought might wipe out his error of a few minutes before. He feigned surprise. "Why there is Father!" he said. "Why, Father, I didn't know you were home! How are you, Father? Welcome home!" Trip acted like a somewhat timid lover as he advanced to the garden where Father was engaged in trying vainly to find a weed.

I had seen to it the day before that he wouldn't find any. It was with me somewhat as with Trip. I had a healthy respect for Father. And Father didn't like weeds.

"Get out of here," said Father, as Trip came close, wagging his tail. But there was a twinkle in Father's eye.

Disappointed, Trip slunk back to his dust bath. But the next day, when Father had gone, he was at his old tricks again. His desire for excitement was stronger than his wish for a good reputation.

Trip's Later Adventures

As time went on young Trip became gradually Old Trip. He grew wiser with the years. I never knew a common dog who seemed to understand as much of the English language as he. My mother talked to him as if he were one of the children. If he came to the front door to be let in she would say, "Why, Trip, I am ashamed of you." His tail would droop and his brown eyes grow sad. "Go around to the back door as you ought." Slowly Trip would go around the house and soon turn up at the back door asking politely to be let into the house.

After a time Trip became proud of his accomplishments. He liked to show off. He was very fond of chasing mice or rats and finally he learned the difference between rats, rabbits, and any other word beginning with *r*. I recall that Mother liked to show visitors how smart Trip was. She would begin something like this:

"That Trip is a good-for-nothing dog. He gets my floor dirty. He is always barking." Trip would look up out of the corner of his eye and then he would rise up and seem to insist that he was innocent. He

was the very best of dogs. His intentions were the highest. What if he did run after the Indians once in a while? A dog had to have a little fun.

"But," went on Mother, "sometimes he is pretty good."

"That's better," wagged Trip, his ears rising a little.

"He likes to hunt r-r-r-r ——," continued Mother. At the sound of the letter *r* Trip's ears would rise more sharply. He gathered himself for a charge.

"Rabbits," said Mother. Trip dropped disgustedly to the floor.

"But," said Mother, "he is really better for r-r- ——." Again the dog got ready.

"Rats," said Mother. The dog charged, wildly barking. Under each piece of furniture, behind the doors, everywhere he went in search of what he was convinced were rats.

Trip was not always as careful about his personal habits as he might have been. He roamed the country as dogs of that time did. Sometimes he would come home smelling like the odor of the cattle barn. At such times, of course, he had to remain outdoors. He would mope for days until he was no longer in disgrace.

As time went on I grew up and finally left home to go to the university. Father and Mother moved to another town. The older boys and girls were away. Old Trip was their care and their companion. He grew gray with the years.

I shall always remember how old Trip acted when I came home from college to visit. It was late in the evening and as I came into the yard, Old Trip charged, barking. It is said that a dog's eyes are not nearly as keen as his nose. Old Trip had lost much of his eyesight and probably a good deal of his sense of smell. But as he came within a few feet of me he always stopped his charge and began to beg my pardon.

"Oh," he seemed to say, "Excuse me. I thought it was a stranger. Here it is my old pal. How glad I am to see you! Welcome home!"

I shall never forget my last adventure with Old Trip. He was very fond of hunting. As a boy I had always taken him rabbit hunting. He was wild with excitement when I got down the gun. On my visit home at the Christmas holidays, my brother and I decided to go rabbit hunting.

"Be careful and don't let Old Trip follow us," we said to Mother as we left the house. Trip was so old and feeble that we knew he could not get through the deep snow.

Brother and I tramped for several miles and killed several rabbits. These we placed in our hunting coats as we got them. We were on our way home when we heard a growling and whining behind us. We looked around and there was Old Trip plowing through the snow. His head was high and he was scolding, but in his mouth he held a rabbit that had fallen from my coat. Old Trip had trailed us through the snow and was just catching up with us as we neared home!

Mother said when we got home that he had scolded for a long time after we had left. Then when the groceries were delivered, Old Trip was ready. He slipped out the door and followed us on his last hunt.

That spring I learned with regret, if not with tears, that Old Trip had passed on. I don't know where dog heaven is, but I'll guess that wherever it is, Old Trip is there and that he is having a good time.

—*Gerald Yoakam.*

Test and Study Exercises

1. Be able to define—tell the meaning of—each of these words used in the story.

personality	lively	ambition
deposited	axles	bristled
previous	imaginary	guilty
convincing	error	regret

2. You have probably had experiences with a dog, a cat, or some other animal. Be ready to tell the class about some such experience.

3. Why did the axles on most of the Indians' wagons squeak?

Suggested Activity

Make an outline of this story. Make it so complete that you could follow it and tell the story in your own words without missing anything important. Copy the outline form given here. Fill it in on your paper, and add to it as much as you need to.

Outline of "Old Trip"

1. My best friend

  (a) Who he was
  (b) His personality
  (c)
  (d)

2.

  (a)
  (b)

Radiator Lions

PREPARATORY NOTE: The boy in this poem couldn't have real animal pets. But he had fun pretending that he did.

George lives in an apartment and
His mother will not let
Him keep a dog or polliwog
Or rabbit for a pet.

So he has Radiator-Lions.
(The parlor is the zoo.)
They love to fight but will not bite
Unless he tells them to.

And days when it is very cold
And he can't go outdoors
They glower and they lower and they
Crouch upon all fours

And roar most awful roarings and
Gurgle loud and mad.
Up their noses water goeses—
That's what makes them bad.

But he loves Radiator-Lions!
He's glad, although they're wild,
He hasn't dogs and polliwogs
Like any other child!

—*Dorothy Aldis.*

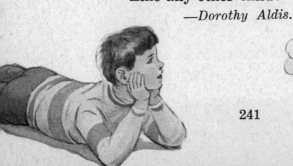

Neighbors

PREPARATORY NOTE: In reading your part in this poem, let your voice be light and jolly.

All: Our neighborhood has lots of dogs—
             You see them everywhere—

Solo 1: Some are very sleek and smooth,

Solo 2: And some have shaggy hair.

Solo 3: Some have long and silky ears
             That flap beside their head,

Solo 4: And others have small pointed ones
             That stand straight up instead.

Solo 5: Some wag a friendly little stub
             That passes for a tail,

Solo 6:   While other dogs wave arching plumes
              As stately as a sail.

All: Like us, dogs *talk* in different ways;

Solo 7:   Some use shrill, yapping tones,

Solo 8:   And nearly all give pleasant growls
              When romping with their bones.

Girls: There are poodle dogs, and terriers,

Boys: Shepherd dogs and chows—

Girls: Some speak in tiny "erps"

Boys: And some in loud "bow-wows!"
                                    —*Louise Abney.*

Test and Study Exercises

1. How many different kinds of dogs are there in the picture on page 242?

2. Read the poem over again quickly, and then write down all the ways in which the poet says dogs talk. Can you suggest any other sounds made by "dog talk"?

Exmoor Star

PREPARATORY NOTE: This is a story of the life and adventures of a pony. The pony was born in Exmoor which is a part of England. A moor is an uncultivated waste land, with plenty of room for running. Exmoor is the name of the moor from which Exmoor Star, the pony, came. When he grew up, he became a star in a circus, and so was called Exmoor Star. The story begins after the pony had been taken from the moor to an English farm.

Adventures of a Pony

A shaggy coat of sober brown, a long shaggy mane that hid my face, a long shaggy tail that swept the ground; that is what I looked like, I suppose, when a baby. I was an Exmoor pony, and most Exmoor ponies that I have seen looked like that.

But I was by no means an ordinary pony. The dark stripe down my back showed that I had good blood in my veins. There was not a speck of white upon my feet or on my legs. There was not a speck of white on my broad forehead. My ears were small and tapering, and my shoulder had an aristocratic slope. My feet were small and pointed. Mother said that I was a pony of which any parent might be proud.

Though she praised my good looks, she never failed to remind me that "Beauty is only skin deep"; that "Handsome is that handsome does"; and that a truly beautiful pony is one that is obedient, good tempered, willing and industrious.

I was a frisky little fellow, but I was anxious to please my mother and when she talked I would answer her with a soft whinny and kiss her, and rub my nose against her velvety skin. When I was in a fairly serious mood I would resolve to do my best to follow her advice.

She was proud of me, and I was equally proud of Mother. Many and many a time, when I was older, I heard my father say that she was the finest mare in the Wilverton Stables.

We,—that is, Father, Mother and I,—belonged to Mr. Day, of Wilverton, near Exeter, and it was at Wilverton that I was born. But in the spring, summer, and autumn, I ran wildly by my mother's side on Exmoor because of the splendid air, and my earliest recollections are of the moor itself. There were about twenty ponies with their mothers, and as we all kept together it was like a big nursery.

Perhaps you think that we were lazy all day long, and had nothing to do but eat and sleep. Not a bit of it! We had our daily schooling, but each mother had her own ideas of teaching her child.

My mother would say to me, "Attend to Mother, my dear, and try to do as I do. Now then—one, two, three, four—lift your foot so, and point your hoofs so, and don't forget to arch your neck." Then I tried to copy her.

"That is right," perhaps she would say, "but you are not arching your neck. Ah! that is better. Now then, attend again; One, two, three, four!"

I attended as long as I could and then I frisked, and mother could not help smiling. She knew well enough that a young foal cannot be quiet for long and she knew well enough that I did not mean to be naughty.

She would say, "Now we will have a change. Come along, my dear, we will race down this side of the meadow and up the other side, and see which will get there first. My legs are stronger than yours, so you shall start from yonder stone, and I will start from this to make it fair. I shall count three, and then at the word 'off'—off we go. Are you ready? Yes? 'One, two, three—off!' "

Down we galloped pell-mell, helter-skelter, faster than the wind. Down the meadow, and up the other side, and both reached the top together. "Well done, my dear!" said Mother, "you will soon be able to run as fast as I!"

When Mother praised me like that I tossed my head and mane and cried, "Hurrah!" Such races were the jolliest fun imaginable.

As we ponies grew older and stronger we often had racing matches together. Sometimes we galloped full speed around the foot of old Dunkery

Beacon, the highest of the Exmoor Hills. Often on our rambles we came upon the pretty red deer, whinnied, "How d'ye do," and were off again like a shot. Often we saw the wild sheep with their curved horns —the sheep were famous climbers—and said, "How d'ye do," to them. Often, however, there was nothing to see but the wide moorland covered with heather and bracken, blackberry bushes and yellow roses.

Once I had a great adventure! It was August, and one morning I was out by myself when I heard in the distance the baying of hounds. I knew that dogs and men ran after the deer, because Mother had told me so, but I had never seen a hunt.

Soon my sharp ears caught the patter of hoofs, and there came by a beautiful dappled mother deer or hind, and a little fawn scampered by her side. The fawn was tired and could not keep up with its mother's long strides. The mother deer looked round, scented the dogs, and knew that she was being overtaken. She said quickly to her child, "Stay here, my darling, till Mother comes back."

Then butting her little one with her head, she tossed it into a thicket of tall bracken, where it was completely hidden. Having done this she set off running as fast as she could, at right angles to the course she had been following. By and by, the dogs came along, sniffing as they went, and when they came to where the mother deer had stopped, they turned off at right angles, and never noticed the little fawn.

Behind the dogs came the hunters in their scarlet coats, but I did not wait any longer. I hurried back to Mother and told her my adventure; "Mother," I said, "will the deer find her child when she comes back?"

"Oh, yes," said Mother, "she is sure to do that."

"If the mother forgets where she hid her child, what would happen?" I asked.

Mother smiled. "Trust a mother to find her child! Don't worry yourself about that!"

"But," I persisted, "a deer has to be very clever to escape."

"Yes," replied Mother. "Sometimes, too, the chase is very exciting. A stag was once chased by the dogs from early morning till late in the afternoon, but he ran so fast, and dodged so cleverly, that they had not been able to overtake him. Poor fellow! His breath grew shorter and shorter, his legs trembled beneath him, his tongue was parched with thirst. He said to himself, 'I am so tired, I can run no farther. What shall I do?'

"Then he remembered that in a stream close by there was a deep pool. 'It is my only chance,' he said, 'I will go there and hide, perhaps the dogs will not find me!'

"He soon reached the pool and plunged into the water. Oh, how cool and refreshing it felt to his weary limbs! He was only just in time, for the dogs almost immediately came up. They sniffed about with their noses to the ground, and barked to each other, 'He entered the water just here. We'll soon catch him!' But though they searched the stream and the banks, the stag was nowhere to be seen!"

"Oh, Mother!" I cried, "do you know where he was?"

248

"Yes, my dear. Where the pool was deepest an elder tree overhung the bank. There, under the shadow of the spreading branches, the stag was crouching. His legs, his body, and his head were under water; only the tip of his nose showed above the surface. He could breathe without being seen."

"Mother, what a clever stag! But, tell me quickly, did they find him?"

"No. Sometimes the dogs seemed to be close to him, and he lay trembling, fearing each moment that he would be discovered. He could hear the huntsmen talking about him. They said, 'It is very strange. What can have become of the stag?' As they could not find him they went home."

"And then, Mother?"

"Then, when the stag thought it quite safe to leave his hiding place, he went home too. You can imagine how eagerly his wife and little ones listened to the story of his adventures, and how glad they were that he had returned to them safe and sound."

I was so pleased that I stamped my hoofs and kissed my mother to show my pleasure.

When I was older I made the acquaintance of a hunting horse, and from him I heard all about fox-hunting. I must not stop to tell you now, because I have more to say first with regard to Exmoor.

Exmoor is close to the Bristol Channel, and sometimes a mist blows in from the Atlantic and completely hides the land. When this happened we could not see a yard before us; we had to smell our way. Ugh! How cold it was! We often shivered in spite of our thick, shaggy coats, for there was little shelter to be found. The mist would frequently last day after day, only parting occasionally, to give us a brief glimpse of the distant hills.

At any time one needs be careful when crossing Exmoor, for the ground in parts is soft and full of bogs. Even in clear weather it is not always easy to see a bog, while a mist hides it completely. In point of danger, heavy and continuous rain is, perhaps, worse than the mist, because it makes the ground more spongy.

The worst bog in Exmoor is soft enough and deep enough to swallow a man on horseback! My companions and I could patter over it easily, because here and there the ground was hard, and our mothers had taught us how to pick out the safe spots, but disastrous results are likely to attend any stranger who accidentally, or recklessly attempts to cross that terrible place.

One day, after a fortnight of pouring rain, I chanced to be on this part of the moor when two horsemen came along. I heard one rider say to the other, "Hello! this looks like boggy ground, we had better be careful!"

Of course, when I heard him say that, I knew that the men were complete strangers to Exmoor, and I wanted to warn them. So I whinnied, and said as plainly as I could, "Stop, stop! Don't attempt to go there, it's dangerous!"

I suppose they did not understand me, for they paid no heed. The horse, however, understood, and was unwilling to go on, but his rider urged him forward, and he obeyed. "It is all right," said the man. "Follow me!"

Hardly had he said the words, when his horse began to flounder. Then its forelegs sank into a deep hole, and the rider was shot head first into the bog. He struggled desperately, and so did the horse, and the horse screamed with fright.

The other man was so close behind him that the hoofs of his horse spattered water. By a tremendous effort he seized his friend just in time and pulled him back, while the horse, like a clever beast, lay on its back and rolled over and over until it reached firm ground. It was indeed a narrow escape!

Besides showing us how to pick our way over boggy ground, our mothers taught us how to be sure-footed on slippery rocks and stones. We could not have had a better practicing ground than the steep little valleys full of rocks and loose stones. These are frightening places to look at, yet with constant practice, and under skillful guidance, we learned to race down them, and neither slipped nor stumbled.

Thus we were constantly learning, and our characters were being gradually formed. To be sure-footed and trustworthy is considered one of the best points of an Exmoor pony. Other good points are health, strength and endurance, and what could help to make us strong and sturdy, long-winded and enduring better than our daily exercises, and our life in the pure bracing air of Exmoor. Of course lessons, however good the teacher, are not much use unless one minds the golden rule:

> In learning, pay attention, do your best;
> Put duty first, and you may leave the rest.
> Work, ponies, work; then play, ponies, play,
> That is the way to be happy and gay.

I cannot tell you what Exmoor is like in winter, for late in the autumn some men came and took Mother and me and our friends down to the comfortable farm at Wilverton. There I saw a great deal of my father, and from him I learned much. He knew the world, for he had traveled in foreign parts. He was an Arabian, and when he grew up, he crossed the wide ocean and came to Devonshire.

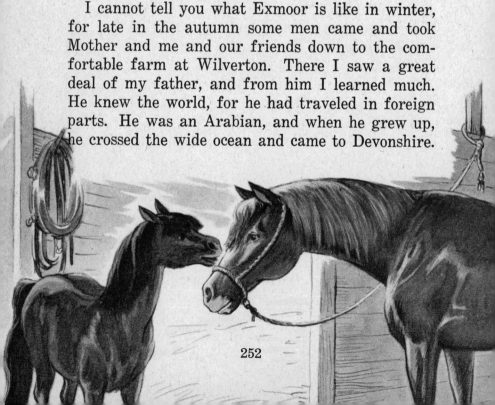

I was eager to know his history, so at the first opportunity I said, "Father, tell me everything about yourself and Arabia."

Father smiled, and said—but that I will tell you in the next chapter.

My Father Tells of His Life in Arabia

"So you wonder what Arabia is like, do you?" said my father. "Well, let me think of the best way to describe it. You know that the sea below Exmoor flows in some places over yellow sands that are perfectly smooth and level?"

"Oh, yes, Father," I said; "is Arabia like that?"

"Yes, something like that. But perhaps you will have a better idea if you try to imagine what Exmoor would be like if it were all sand instead of grass, with no river or stream or pool to be seen, and maybe not a drop of water for miles and miles."

"No water!" I cried. "It must be a strange country."

"Yes," said Father, "Arabia consists mainly of desert; only here and there, where there is a little water, there are a few green spots called oases. Arabia is much warmer than England. The sun shines all day long, and the sky is blue and without a cloud.

"The people who live there are called Arabs. They are brown in color and their eyes are black. They wear long flowing robes with a girdle around the waist; around their heads they wear a long piece of cloth for a turban. In England people live in big

253

houses, with many doors and windows but the Arabs dwell in canvas tents, and sleep on the ground."

"It sounds very strange," I said; "but I am more interested in the ponies. Do they sleep on the ground, or in boxes called stalls as we do here?"

"On the ground," said Father. "I belonged," he continued, "to a chief, or sheik, as he is called, named Nabee, and was treated just like one of the family. The care Arabs take of horses is surprising."

"How do you mean?" I said.

"Well," said my father, "soon after I was born I was given two or three eggs to eat, and my hoofs were rubbed with salt and desert herbs in order to make them hard. My ears were tied together with string so that they might grow straight, and every day my mane and tail were carefully washed. When I was six months old I was given sometimes cow's milk, sometimes ewe's milk, and sometimes camel's milk, so that my coat might become smooth and glossy. I lived in my master's tent with the family. The children and I were great friends. We played together, and they gave me cakes made of flour and milk and dates. They kissed and patted me as the family pet, and I was as happy as the day was long. By and by my master tested me, to see if I was a well-formed horse.

"He made me stand upright on all four legs and drink from a stream that was on the same level as the ground.

"I drank the water without bending my knees; for if I had been badly formed I should have bent my knees in drinking."

When Father told me that I could not help looking at my own legs, and Father laughed.

"I was wondering," I said, "if I could drink without bending my knees."

"I guessed as much," said my father. "I think you could, but you can easily try when an opportunity occurs!"

"Well, Father, please go on."

"I was taught," he continued, "to do many things that are necessary for a pony's education in Arabia. One of the first things I learned was to do this."

So saying, Father reared upright, and solemnly walked about on his hind legs, to my great astonishment and delight.

"After I could do this well, I was taught this." So saying he leaped into the air, all four feet leaving the ground at the same moment.

"When I did this easily," said he, "I had to jump with my master on my back. As I leaped, he threw his long gun into the air and caught it again before my feet touched the ground."

"Father, that is wonderful!" I cried, and he continued his story.

"Here was another thing I learned to do with my master on my back." And Father gradually bent his front legs until he knelt gracefully upon the ground.

I had no idea that my father knew so many wonderful tricks, and I felt very proud of him. "Does Mother know how clever you are?" I said.

At that he laughed. "I really don't know," he said.

Then he continued: "When I was two years old, my master put a bit into my mouth, and said to me,

'Now I am going to prove you, to see if you are a worthy son of a worthy father and grandfather; so mind you do your very best.'

"Then he sprang lightly upon my back, and away he went, like the wind. For several hours we kept on at top speed over the desert sands without once stopping. Suddenly a river appeared before us. Still my master urged me forward, and so I plunged in. There was a very strong current, and it was very hard work to swim against it, but at length I managed to reach the other side of the river.

"There the sheik got off and made me take a long drink. Then he kissed and stroked me, and called me his 'treasure.' I had done well, so you know I was very pleased."

"And after that, Father?" I said, eager to hear more.

"Some time after that," he said, "I was taken to hunt the ostrich."

"Ostrich?" I asked. "Is that like a red deer?"

Father smiled. "No," he said, "an ostrich is a big bird."

"Bigger than an owl?" said I, for that was the largest bird I knew.

"Yes," said Father, "bigger than twenty owls rolled into one. Its legs are uncommonly long, and it runs with great swiftness, using its wings as well as its legs. It is one of the birds that cannot fly."

"And did you catch him, Father?"

"Yes. When we first saw the ostrich it was on the sandy plain, but when it saw us it ran off at full speed towards the distant hills, hoping to escape.

Fast as it ran, we were there first; so the ostrich turned and fled in another direction, until at length it was so tired that it could go no further, and was easily caught. My master was very pleased, for a horse must be exceedingly swift to run down an ostrich as I had done."

"Father," I said, "have you had any other adventures?"

"Yes, I have had a great many in my time," said Father.

"What was the very greatest?" I asked eagerly.

My father considered, then he said: "I hardly know, but here is one. There was a man of another tribe of Arabs, and his name was Daher. He had heard a great deal about me, and was very anxious indeed to own me. He offered my master in exchange for me as many as twelve camels and two hundred and fifty sheep. Though this was a very tempting offer, my master would not part with me."

"I don't wonder at that!" said I. "But Father, you spoke of sheep and camels. I know what sheep are, because I have seen them on Exmoor. What is a camel?"

"An animal," said Father, "with a hump on its back. It has a kind of deep pocket inside it, which will hold a great deal of water. When the camel is thirsty it can use the water from the bag. For this reason, and because it can walk easily on sand with a heavy load on its back, and because it is very patient and enduring, the camel is of the very greatest use to the Arabs."

"I see," said I, "and then what happened, Father?"

"Well, when Daher found he could not get me by fair means, he determined to steal me. In order that he should not be known, he disguised himself. He made his face much darker by staining it with the juice of herbs; he tied up his legs, so that he might appear to be lame, and he dressed himself in rags like a beggar. Then he lay down by the side of the road where my master and I would pass, and waited. As soon as he saw us he began to cry for help. My master felt so sorry that he told him to get up on the horse and he would then take him to his tent and feed and care for him. The pretended cripple said, 'I thank you with all my heart, but, alas, I cannot get up without help.'

"Then my master dismounted and with a great deal of trouble, managed to lift the man on my back. No sooner was he firmly seated than off he dashed, shouting to my master, 'I am Daher, and your horse is now mine!'

"'Stop! stop!' cried my master, 'and hear first what I have to say.'" So Daher stopped. "'You now have my horse, but I beg of you not to let anyone know how you got him.'

"'And why should I not?'" said Daher.

"'Because,' replied my master, 'some other person really poor and afflicted might be left without any help. If you tell the tale, then no one will do a single act of kindness for fear of being cheated like me.'

"Upon hearing these words, Daher was filled with shame. He said, 'I see now that I have done a very wrong thing, and I am sorry for it.' Then he got off my back, and led me to my master."

"How glad I am, Father," said I, "that all turned out well in the end. But do go on and tell me more."

Father considered. "Well," he said, "here is another adventure which shows how much an Arab thinks of the color of his horse, and of how his horse is fed. I was once far away from home with my master and his three sons, who were fighting against another tribe. It chanced that a large number of the enemy came upon us unawares, and we had to flee for our lives. I carried the master. The country in which we were was hilly, and we were trying to keep in the shade as much as possible.

"By and by the sheik called to his eldest son, 'Look behind you, and tell me what horses you see in the front of the enemy.' So his son looked, and replied 'White horses.'"

"'That is well,' said his father, 'let us make for the sunny side, and they will soon be exhausted.' He knew that white horses easily tire if exposed to great heat. After we had gone some distance further, the sheik called to his second son, 'Look over your shoulder, and tell me what horses you see in the front of the enemy.' The second son looked and replied, 'Black horses.' "

" 'That is right,' said his father. 'Let us make for yonder stony ground and then we have no need to be afraid, for black horses cannot walk barefoot over stones.' Again we went on, and after a time the master called to his third son, 'Look back, and say what horses you can see in front of the enemy.' "

"He replied, 'I see dark chestnuts and dark bays.' "

" 'In that case, ride fast, my children!' cried the sheik. 'Now might we be overtaken had we not fed our horses upon barley all the summer through.' Away we raced, faster than before, and sure enough, the enemy was left far behind."

Then I asked Father why the color of a horse seemed to matter.

"I do not know," he said, "but I believe it is true that dark bay and brown horses are the best:

"If a horse has one white stocking—buy;
If a horse has two—be very shy;
If a horse has four—then pass it by."

"And as to a feed of barley," said Father, "there is nothing like it. My master was right there; though sometimes, before going on a long journey, I have been given roasted meat, that I might better bear fatigue."

"Father, you were so happy and well cared for, how was it," said I, "that you left Arabia?"

Father sighed. "My kind master died very suddenly," he replied, "and I was sold to an English chief. I had to say good-by to my old home, and follow my new master to Mecca, the 'Mother of Towns,' as the Arabs call it. There, for the first time, I saw houses built of stone. From Mecca I was taken to Yedda, a busy town, where the buildings are all white. Here I had my first glimpse of the great salt water, for Yedda is a port on the Red Sea. From there I sailed in a native vessel to Suez, and then went by train to Port Said. Here I was put on board a very large steamer. The manner of doing it," he said, with a merry twinkle in his eye, "you would have thought quite an adventure.

"First of all a bandage was tied over my eyes, and then I was put into a little box that was just big enough to hold me. I wondered what was going to happen, when up—up in the air I went, hoisted by a machine called a crane. Then suddenly I seemed to drop—it made me feel quite dizzy and queer— down—down. Then the bandage was taken off my eyes, and I found myself on the deck of a vessel!"

"Oh, Father, weren't you dreadfully frightened?"

"Well," said he, "I must confess that I felt a little nervous; however I was quite safe. From Port Said I sailed to London, and there I was bought by Mr. Day, and came to live at Wilverton."

"They must have thought a great deal of you, Father, to have paid so much and brought you so far!"

261

"Yes, but many people consider Arab horses to be the very best in the world, and are willing to pay a large sum for what they consider a first-rate animal.

"And now that I have told you something about myself and Arabia, I have just a word of advice to give you. Don't disgrace your father. Be obedient, good tempered, willing, and industrious, and always do your very best. You will not have your parents always with you, but before very long you will have to make your own way in the world."

Here our talk ended.

Test and Study Exercises

1. Copy the three sentences below that best tell the main thoughts in the story so far.

The pony was brought up on an English moor.

The pony saw a deer hunt.

The pony's mother taught him many things.

The pony's father could run fast.

The pony's father gave him good advice.

2. What is a moor?

3. What was the name of the man who owned the pony and his father and mother?

4. Where did the pony's father say the Arabian ponies slept?

5. Look up the meaning of any words in the list below that you do not know already. Be able to use each of these words correctly in a sentence.

obedient	scampered	persisted
shelter	frequently	occasionally
guidance	endurance	gradually
opportunity	exhausted	fatigue

6. In what danger were the two men whom the pony tried to warn in the moor?

Suggested Activity

Be able to tell in your own words what each of these sentences means.

A truly beautiful pony is one that is obedient, good tempered, willing and industrious.

We often shivered in spite of our thick, shaggy coats, for there was little shelter to be found.

Besides showing us how to pick our way over boggy ground, our mothers taught us how to be surefooted on slippery rocks and stones.

Breaking In

PREPARATORY NOTE: Exmoor Star was sold to a new master, and went to a new home. But the new master was a good one and the pony learned quickly how to get along with him. In this part called "Breaking In," you will find some interesting facts about how horses are trained. Later the pony has more thrilling adventures.

One morning, not long after I had been separated from my parents, I had a good chance to see Mr. Bryce, my new master. He was standing quite still, not paying any attention to me, and so I took the opportunity to have a good look at him.

He was a middle-aged man, with a nice, kind face. He had nothing in his hands, but over one of his arms there hung a rope, and two or three straps. By and by he took a few steps very slowly in my direction. At first I was prepared to run, but when I saw that he did not move his arms or hands, and seemed so gentle, I felt reassured.

After a time, he came quite close to my side. I sniffed at him, and he very quietly put his hand on my neck, and stroked and patted me, and said pleasantly: "So ho, my beauty! Gently, old boy!"

It felt very pleasant, indeed, for who does not like to be patted?

Gradually he drew me towards him; again I sniffed at him, and made a step in his direction. I wondered why he pulled my head, and then it struck me that perhaps he wanted me to follow him. I did so. Thus we began to understand each other.

We walked up and down together in the same quiet manner for some time. My master kept talking to me, and showed me the rope and straps that hung on his arm. So, to please him, I looked carefully at them, and sniffed at them; there was certainly no harm in them.

After again stroking and patting me, he went away; but I followed him to the gate of the paddock, and whinnied after him, "I like you very much; come soon and see me again."

On hearing my voice he turned, and smiled as if he understood. Sure enough, in the afternoon he came again to see me. He stroked my head and neck, and patted me; and again he showed me his straps and let me smell them. Then he stroked my chest and my legs, which was most soothing and pleasant. I guessed that he wanted me to lift my foot so I drew up the one that was nearest to him. He slipped one of the straps over it somehow, and fastened the strap to my knee, and then I found that I could only hobble along on three legs. It really was queer!

My master fastened another strap to my other knee and by and by, as I lifted the front leg that was free, the foot of that leg was somehow caught up too, and then the strangest thing happened. As I had nothing whatever now to stand on in front, down I went on my knees! It did not hurt me, you know, the least bit, but I was astonished, and then my master happened to lean against me gently, and over I rolled on my side. This was still more astonishing. I seemed to have lost the use of my limbs. I tried to rise, but could not. Then I felt a little afraid, and made desperate efforts to regain my feet, but I only tired myself, and the next time that I rolled over, Mr. Bryce came and sat on me.

"Well," I thought to myself, "you must be an unusually strong and clever man. You seem to be able to do what you like with me. What you do is decidedly odd, but at the same time I like to be patted and stroked." Then and there I made the very wise resolve to do just what my master wanted.

The next day when he came into the paddock and held out his hand and called me, I ran to him at once, and besides being stroked and patted, I was rewarded with a lump of sugar, so I knew that I had pleased him.

Every day my master came in the morning and afternoon to see me, and he stayed with me about half an hour. He always talked pleasantly to me, and we soon became acquainted. Once he brought with him a short piece of polished steel to show me. "There," he said, "that is what is called a bit. Take a good look at it, and smell it."

I did so.

"Now," he said, "you shall have it in your mouth." Then he warmed it a little, and pushed it between my teeth.

"Not very nice, eh?" said he. "Never mind, you will soon get used to it."

Another time he brought me something made of leather. "This," he said, "is for you to wear around your neck. But examine it carefully for yourself."

So I felt it with my nose and smelled it, and when my master thought I saw that there was nothing harmful he slipped it over my head and on my neck. It felt a little awkward, but it was softly padded, and so did not hurt me in the least.

When I was quite used to my halter, my master showed me a large flat piece of leather. "This is called a saddle," he said.

After I had examined it to my satisfaction, he rested it on my back, and he put it on again in the afternoon. The next day he fastened it on with a strap, which came under my middle. We got on famously together, because he always chatted to me and explained things.

One day, when he had put on my saddle and bridle he said, "Now, old boy, I want you to give me a ride."

So after again patting and stroking me he got on my back, to my great surprise, and I carried him around the paddock. I did feel proud!

Just about this time, I heard him remark to Tom, who worked at the stable, "He is as good-tempered, affectionate, and intelligent a pony as I have ever handled, and he is well broken in now!"

"Hello, old fellow! What has become of you? I want you!"

I started and cried, "There is the master calling me!"

I ran to the gate, pushed up the latch with my nose, pulled the gate towards me with my hoof, and managed to squeeze through. Then I ran to my master. "Here I am," I whinnied.

My master patted me and gave me a lump of sugar. Then he turned to a man by his side and said, "This is the pony that Tom told you about. It seems that he has opened the gate more than once, though Tom assures me that he always fastens it securely. He is a beauty, and as sensible as a judge. His father was an Arabian, his mother an Exmoor, so that he has an excellent pedigree. I believe that there is money in that pony, Mr. Jinniver."

"Well, there may be, but then again there may not. The circus is a risk, but I am prepared to take a little extra risk here, for I've taken a fancy to him. Let me see his paces."

So Tom was called, and he trotted me up and down and showed me off. And then the stranger, Mr. Jinniver, came and patted me and stroked me. He felt me all over, he examined my teeth, and all the while he talked pleasantly to me. "How would you like to be a circus horse?" he said.

As I did not understand in the least what he was talking about, I rubbed my nose silently against his sleeve, for I liked him already. Having satisfied himself apparently as far as possible, he turned to Mr. Bryce. "What is your price?" he asked.

"I want twenty-five guineas," said my master, "and I won't take one farthing less. I warrant him sound, of course, in wind and limb."

"Very well," said Mr. Jinniver. "I'll take him and see if I can make a star of him."

I did not understand what he meant.

"Well," said Mr. Bryce, "he is undoubtedly clever and intelligent, good-tempered, and willing, and I would not part with him unless I felt sure that he would be in good hands."

"I quite appreciate your remarks," replied Mr. Jinniver; "I have had a far larger experience than most men in the training of all sorts of animals, and the longer I live the surer I am that patience and kind treatment will always accomplish far more than harsh words and the whip."

Later in the day Mr. Bryce said, "Tom, you know where Jinniver's Theater is?"

"Yes, sir," said Tom, with a grin.

"Well, I want you to take the pony over there in the morning. I said he should be there before many people were about, so you had better start not later than half past six, and deliver him into Mr. Jinniver's own hands."

"All right, sir," said Tom, "it shall be done."

So early the next morning I left my kind master and set out to try my fortune as a circus pony, and perhaps become a star, whatever that might be.

As we went along I wondered what a circus was like. It was no use, of course, for me to ask Tom,

as he would not understand me. I believed that all
sorts of animals performed there, but that was the
extent of my information. Patience! I should soon
know.

It was a place of very great importance, if one
might judge from the large area of ground which
it covered. There were various buildings connected
with it, but the great round theater itself was the
principal one. On it was painted in great staring
letters:

JINNIVER'S

The walls were covered with wonderful colored
pictures showing deeds of daring by men and women
and animals, and there were all sorts of notices to
the public, each one headed:

JINNIVER'S WORLD-RENOWNED
CIRCUS

Tom did not stop to read them, but went straight
to the back entrance and asked for Mr. Jinniver.

I Join a Circus

That very morning my training commenced, and,
as the training of a performing pony is very different from being "broken in," I will tell you a little
of how it is done. My new instruction was the more
interesting to me because it reminded me of my

father's accomplishments as taught him by the Arabs.

Here are some of my tricks: I learned to be driven without any reins; at the word of command, to lie down, to sit up, to walk upon my hind legs; to bow, and to say "yes" or "no" by shaking my head; to kiss and lick my master; to roll over, and to "laugh." I learned how to pick up a handkerchief, how to stand on a box, how to beat a drum, and ring a bell.

Now I was taught to "kiss" in this way: horses, I dare say you know, are fond of salt, so my master would put a little salt on his cheek or on his lips, and hold out his face towards me. I saw and smelled the salt, and licked it off. After I had done this a great number of times my master held his face toward me without any salt on it, until I understood that I was to lick or "kiss" him, and when I guessed correctly and did right, I was always rewarded with a lump of sugar, or a carrot, or something else that I liked. Now there, you see, the intelligence of the pony comes in; a clever animal will soon get to understand what is required of him, but a stupid one never will.

The handkerchief trick is taught in this way; my master approached me, carrying a clean white handkerchief. Passing his right hand under my chin, he caught hold of my nose from the other side to steady me, then with his left hand he pressed the handkerchief between my teeth, making me hold it by shutting my jaws together. If I dropped the handkerchief he lightly struck my teeth together to show me that I had done wrong. So he kept offering me the handkerchief until I learned to take it between my teeth.

After this my master held the handkerchief towards me on the point of a stick, while at the same time he gently pricked me on the breast with a pin which he had concealed in his hand. When I felt the prick I made a grab at the handkerchief and caught it in my mouth.

This was repeated a number of times, and the handkerchief was gradually held lower and lower until at length I had learned to pick it up off the floor.

It took a good many weeks before I was nearly perfect in these various tricks, and until I was perfect I was not allowed to perform in public. I was often in the theater, however, when performances were given, so that I might become accustomed to the sight and sound of a large crowd of people.

There were a number of ponies employed by Mr. Jinniver. Twelve of them drew the triumphal car in the procession that paraded the streets every afternoon wherever we went.

The queen of the triumphal car was "Fifine." She was very beautiful and very clever, and she sat high up on a golden throne with a scepter in her hand. The giant Magog and the dwarf Mustard-Seed were her attendants.

The procession was led by a band, the musicians being sixteen wild Indians in their war paint. Behind them marched two camels, behind them two ostriches, behind them two elephants, and then came the triumphal car with Queen Fifine.

In the circus a number of trained ponies were used. They cantered around the ring while four ladies dressed as fairies rode upon their backs. Sometimes the riders balanced themselves on one toe, sometimes they rode two ponies at once, sometimes they danced, or jumped through paper hoops held out by the clown.

Queen Fifine was very clever in walking the tight rope, and she performed most daring feats on the trapeze. Several times she had seen me training, and one day she said to Mr. Jinniver, "That is a beautiful pony. I should like to have him, may I?"

"All right," said he, "you shall bring him out!"

So after that she helped teach me tricks, and we grew quite fond of each other.

One day Mr. Jinniver said to Fifine, "Have you thought of a name for your favorite?"

"No," replied the queen, "but he will need to have one. Let me see! Ah, I have it! He is going to be a star pony—call him the 'Exmoor Star.'"

My first performance in public was a great success. The queen drove me in her chariot without the use of reins. When she asked me if I would not prefer to leave Jinniver's, I emphatically shook my head. When she said, "You are a very clever pony, aren't you?" I nodded, "Yes, indeed I am!" When she said, "Whom do you love best in the world?" I gave her a kiss. We played seesaw together, and I went through all the other tricks without a mistake. When the people clapped and cried, "Bravo, Exmoor Star," I laughed, and then the applause was tremendous.

Afterwards when the queen praised me and petted me I did indeed feel pleased, and I heard her say to Mr. Jinniver, "I have a grand idea. I'll make that pony a good actor, see if I don't."

I Distinguish Myself

You will remember Queen Fifine said that she had a grand idea. So she had, and she and I spent a part of each day in trying to work it out successfully. For weeks we practiced patiently, and at last we were ready to perform before the public. Programs were printed with big letters at the top which read:

274

ONE ACT DRAMA

MARVELOUS REALISTIC SENSATION

THE BURNING HOUSE

WHAT WILL BECOME OF HER?

A scene was given of a house on fire. Thick clouds of smoke poured from the windows. Two or three fire engines were pumping water in a vain attempt to put out the fire.

A fire escape was put up against the front of the house, and several people were rescued by the heroic efforts of the firemen, who ran up the ladder at the risk of their lives.

Suddenly a thrill of horror passed through the crowd of onlookers, for a woman—Queen Fifine—was seen at one of the top windows shrieking loudly for help. Alas! The ladder was too short to reach her; the staircase was in such a blaze that the firemen dared not attempt to climb it. Could nothing be done to rescue the poor woman from her perilous position?

Ah! The faithful pony, the lady's favorite steed —that was I—heard and recognized the voice of his beloved mistress. Rushing from his stable, he saw the danger. He entered the house, and regardless of flames and smoke, mounted the blazing stairs, and reached his mistress. Quickly she sprang upon his back and clung to his mane, and so he carried her downstairs, out of the house and out of danger. Immediately after that, the top floor where she had been fell in with a crash. She had been rescued just in time! The scene was the more remarkable, as it is a well-known fact that horses have a great dread of fire.

The act was a great success. Nothing like it had ever been attempted before. And so the people crowded to see the wonderful performance of which I was the hero.

Naturally, Mr. Jinniver was delighted.

"Well, your Majesty," he said to Queen Fifine, "you have carried out your plans splendidly. I most heartily congratulate you and your very clever pupil."

"Is he not a beauty?" she said, as she stroked my neck. "But we hope to show you something even more surprising, don't we, Exmoor Star?"

Seeing that I was expected to say "Yes" I bravely bowed, whereupon Mr. Jinniver and Fifine laughed, and I thought it only polite to laugh too.

The next scheme of Her Majesty was far more complicated than the first, and in practicing for it we were often very tired.

Fifine's idea was to give a number of scenes from the life of a horse, showing his career from youth to old age. Of course each scene was practiced separately, and only when we felt ourselves perfect in one did we go on to another.

At the end of eight months we were ready to give our first rehearsal performance. Scene one: "The Hunter." The stage curtain rose and brought to view a fine family mansion. In front of the house a number of horsemen in scarlet hunting costumes rode to and fro. At the foot of a flight of steps, a splendid horse, held by a groom, waited impatiently, pawing the ground. The horse was I. Down the steps came a lady in a riding habit. Queen Fifine. She stroked and patted my glossy velvet coat, and sprang to the saddle.

When the dogs, a number of beautiful fox hounds, came up, the huntsman gave the signal and off we went. By and by the dogs, who were trained for the purpose, started a fox and gave chase. The huntsmen cried "Tally ho!" to spur them on.

Away we dashed, over hedges and ditches, rocks and stones, until, in the course of the hunt, we came to a peasant's cottage. The door stood open, the fox was hard pressed, so in he popped, and leaped into the lap of an old woman, to her great surprise.

"Poor fellow!" she said, and took him in her arms. "You are quite safe now; no one shall hurt you."

After that we all went home, and that was the end of the scene.

Scene two showed a London cab stand. There stood a cab and in the shafts was a wretched, broken-down horse. You would not have known me, I feel sure; but all the same, it was I. The horse's head hung down, as if he had not the strength to lift it up; his poor ribs showed through his skin—I was cleverly painted to give me that appearance—his joints were so stiff that his legs were bowed at the knees, as he stood mournfully on three legs so as to give the fourth a little rest. He looked, I assure you, the very picture of misery.

Then four people came along, and hailed the cab. They crowded inside it, all four, though there was room for only two; a heavy box was pulled up on to the roof, the driver climbed to his seat, crack went the whip on the horse's poor ribs, and away he shuffled as well as he could.

But that sort of life could not last very long, and scene three showed a still more miserable animal. The poor creature was harnessed to a cart laden with bricks. As it stood waiting for its drunken driver, a child held out a bunch of grass, which it was thankful to nibble.

Then its master staggered up, and began to beat it with a heavy whip. The horse—it was I—took a few steps, then tottered and fell, and though blows were showered on it, it was unable to get up.

A crowd gathered round. "Shame, shame!" they cried, "the horse is dying!"

Just then a lady who was passing by saw the dying animal, and coming closer, recognized it as the very same horse that, years ago, used to take her fox hunting. Kneeling down in the dirty road, she took the animal's head in her lap. "Oh, my dear old favorite!" she said, crying. "What would I not give to restore you once more to health and strength!"

Suddenly a fairy appeared, dressed in spangles, and waved her wand over the dying horse. "Rise," she said, "and be young again!"

At these words the horse sprang to its feet with a bound, no longer looking half-starved and wretched, but sleek and glossy. Then the lady jumped on his back and rode off at a gallop.

My Training as a Polo Pony

Soon after this, I was bought by Lord Darcourt to be used as a polo pony. In this training my previous education helped me very much. You will remember that I had learned to be ridden without bit or bridle. The pressure of my rider's leg was sufficient to direct me to the right or left.

Another thing I learned was bending, and this was very important. The manner of instruction was curious and interesting.

A number of tall, thin sticks were stuck in the ground in one line about eight feet distant from each other, and they were so placed that they could be easily knocked down. I started at a slow canter about twenty yards from them and zigzagged between them, taking first a stick on the near side and then one on the off side, and I had to pass them as closely as possible without knocking them over.

When I learned to do this well at a canter I learned to do it at a gallop. My master was very pleased and always had an apple, a carrot, or a lump of sugar in his pocket with which to reward me.

When I had thoroughly learned to trot and canter, to change legs just at the right moment, to turn fast and clearly at the will of my rider, to start or stop instantly, I was introduced to the stick and ball.

I was encouraged to smell and examine them closely, until I was assured they were very harmless things. Then my master got on my back and began to hit the ball about with his stick as I walked. After a few days of this he hit the ball about while I trotted; then, after a longer time still, when I galloped.

When I had mastered all this, he hit the ball backwards so that I had to turn quickly as soon as the ball was struck, and gradually I learned to turn on such occasions without being told to do so.

After this I went through my various exercises while other ponies were running hither and thither, and was taught to mind my own business and not to excite myself as to what they were doing.

Last of all, to give me confidence, I had to meet two ponies coming towards me at a gallop, one on each side of me. At first they were wide apart, but gradually they came closer and closer to me until they almost touched me.

Up to now I had not been particularly interested in what was required of me, and thought the whole business somewhat silly, but my master was very patient and kind and I was anxious to please him.

You may imagine that so much galloping and violent exercise made me very hot indeed. In such a condition I could easily catch cold, but my master was very careful to look after me. After he got off, he would give orders to have my girths loosened and to have me led up and down until I was cool. Then I was put into my stable with my saddle still on, and it was not taken off for an hour or more.

Exmoor Star to the Rescue

One day I heard my master say, "We are going to have a storm!"

I could have told him that! How could I tell? Oh, easily enough by the feel of the air and by the smell of the storm. I cannot explain so that you would understand. Animals just seem to know when a bad storm is coming.

Sure enough it began to blow before evening. The wind whistled and shrieked, the sky became darker and darker, the lightning flashed in a way that I did not like at all, and the thunder that followed made me jump. Then the rain came down in torrents. The sea was rising every minute and I could hear in the pauses of the storm the breakers dashing themselves to foam on the rocks. It was unpleasant but it really did not matter much to me, as I was well sheltered.

All night long the storm raged. I heard it now and then when an unusually loud peal of thunder or a flash of lightning wakened me.

Soon after daybreak there came the sound of a different kind of thunder, the boom of a gun, and at intervals of about a minute the sound was repeated. Then I heard hurrying footsteps and shouts of "A wreck! A wreck!"

I heard my master's voice asking, "Where?"

"On the rocks," was the reply, "about a quarter of a mile off shore."

"I will come!" said my master. He saddled and bridled me as quickly as possible and we set out for the scene of the disaster.

On reaching the shore we found that it was difficult to make out anything seawards, partly on account of the gloom, partly on account of the driving spray. Every now and then we could see the white top of a great wave, as it broke into foam, and roared landwards.

A vivid flash of lightning lit up the scene, and there, on the cruel rocks, was a ship, and a mast with human beings clinging to it.

"What is being done?" said my master to the few people who had gathered on the beach. He had to shout at the top of his voice to make himself heard above the storm.

"Nothing!" said the man addressed, sadly. "We have no boats, and no means of reaching the ship!"

"Well, I've a plucky horse under me, and I mean to try!" said my master.

"What, swim?" cried the man. "It would be madness to attempt it in such a sea!"

"Nonsense!" replied my master, "something must be attempted. We can't see those poor fellows drown before our eyes, can we, Exmoor Star?"

"No, indeed, I should think not," I whinnied.

Then my master looked carefully at my bridle and at my saddle, stroked and patted me, mounted, and rode boldly into the sea.

On the word of a polo pony I can tell you it did look like a mad thing to attempt. However, I thought my master knew best, so in I plunged. The very first wave nearly knocked me over, but my master kept me steady. In a short time I managed to hold my nose above water without choking, and so swam forward toward the wreck, my master leaving my head free, and guiding me by the pressure of his legs.

How we managed to cross those great raging billows is more than I can tell you, but by and by, we neared the vessel. There were twelve men clinging to the mast, and when they saw us they gave a feeble cheer.

"Here's a chance for two of you," shouted my master, pulling up under the sheltered side of the wreck, and two sailors lowered themselves into the sea.

"Cling to the stirrups," said Lord Darcourt. So one man clung to my right stirrup and one to my left. Then I struck out for the shore while the two men swam as well as they could, and my master guided me. After a hard struggle we managed to reach the shore. Hurrah! two lives saved!

We only waited a few minutes to get our breath, and then plunged again into the sea, struggled back to the wreck, and with another couple of men clinging to the stirrups, returned to shore.

Six times we made that terrible journey, twelve times we crossed between the wreck and the shore. My master again and again patted, and praised, and encouraged me, and in the end all the twelve men were saved.

Our work ended, my master fainted from weakness, and I was so exhausted that at last I had only just enough strength to totter to the land, but willing hands helped me up the beach.

That night I felt very ill; I had terrible pains in one of my hind legs, so that I could not help groaning a great deal.

My master came to see me in the morning and was greatly distressed at my appearance. I licked his hand and tried to tell him about my trouble. "Ah," he said, "I see your leg is badly swollen. You must have the doctor."

There was no doctor anywhere near, so my master took me to the town where the other ponies were. I remember how shocked my friends were at my appearance.

The horse doctor soon came to see me. He said to my master, "This horse has hurt himself by his violent exercise. A muscle is very badly strained. He won't be able to do any more work."

My master stroked and patted me, and I am pretty sure that he cried. You see, I was his favorite. "Poor old boy," he said, "you and I won't play polo together any more, and what shall I do without you? But I am proud of you, Exmoor Star."

I was sorry when he said we should not play together again, but I was pleased that I had done my duty. And my friends all said how very sorry they were.

"Polo won't be worth playing any more now," said Dan Connor.

"No, indeed it won't," echoed the others.

I think it is very pleasant to be thought well of by one's friends, even if they do exaggerate a little, don't you?

And I was well looked after I assure you! I had a most comfortable stable, the best of food, and a beautiful paddock in which I could lounge about and rest. My life was one great holiday! I actually had a medal given to me by the Royal Humane Society, and I often wore it round my neck.

Yes, and do you know, people who had heard the story of the wreck would come, sometimes, quite a long distance to see me, and my master would tell them: "Yes, this is Exmoor Star, the pony that saved twelve people from drowning. He was the finest polo player in the world."

Then, of course, I smiled my best circus smile.

—*A. E. Bonser.*

Test and Study Exercises

1. Make an outline of the part of the story that tells about the breaking in of Exmoor Star.

2. What did Mr. Jinniver say was the best way to train animals?

3. What is the meaning of each of these words?

paddock	hobble	astonishing
polished	affectionate	various
procession	heroic	perilous
ditches	peasant	scene

4. How did Star get to Jinniver's?

5. Make a list of the tricks that Star learned in the circus.

6. How did Exmoor Star get his name?

7. How did Star's circus training help him as a polo pony?

8. How did all of Exmoor Star's training help him do his last great act of bravery?

9. What part of the story of Exmoor Star do you like best? Why?

Suggested Activities

1. How much, in American money, did Mr. Jinniver pay for Star? Find out, first, what one guinea is worth in our money.

2. Be able to describe Star's burning-house act in your own words.

3. If you have seen a circus horse do an interesting trick, be ready to tell the class about it.

More Word Friends

PREPARATORY NOTE: Perhaps you haven't thought of words as friends. Like friends they are helpful. But before people are your real friends you must know them well. If words are to help you, you must know them well.

The consonants are sounds that require tongue, lips, teeth, and palate to make them. They are not free and open like the vowels. But they, too, are often slighted in our word friends.

Do you always use correct consonants when you speak? Have you ever said *'em* for *them* as "I like 'em" for "I like them"? Or have you ever said "just like 'at" when you meant "just like that"? Beginning consonants are often slighted. Occasionally middle consonants are left out; and very often, somebody is leaving off the end of a word friend. This is just as bad as having your friends leave out part of your name.

Do you like *licorice* candy? Do you buy it at the store? How do you pronounce the last syllable—as if it were *lic-o-rish?* Check this word in your dictionary and see how it should be sounded. Maybe you have been right all along—and maybe not!

Do you always watch the final *t*'s and *d*'s in these words: jus*t*, mus*t*, lef*t*, wep*t*, slep*t*, swep*t*, bes*t*, les*t*, nes*t*, wes*t*, aske*d*? Consonants are important, just as vowels are, if you would stay on the best of terms with your word friends; yet nearly every day somebody is leaving off the end of some word friend's name.

Read these words aloud, very carefully, sounding all the *-ing* endings, so that your speech will be correct:

anything	making
asking	morning
coming	nothing
crouching	parting
doing	racing
enduring	reading
exciting	running
following	smiling
going	sniffing
learning	something

Too often their endings are chopped off. Use them in sentences so they won't feel neglected.

Test and Study Exercises

1. In making consonant sounds correctly, what speech organs do you have to use?

2. Answer the question in the fourth paragraph of this word story.

3. Write or speak sentences containing each of the words listed in the two columns above.

You'll Find Them in Australia

PREPARATORY NOTE: An animal that carries her baby in
a fur-lined pocket, a bird whose hide is used for rugs—
this story tells of these and other interesting creatures.

Australia, the island continent on the other side
of the world, is a land full of interesting things. Perhaps the most interesting of all are its animals, its
birds, and its reptiles.

If you could see all these creatures of Australia
and of Tasmania, the neighbor island on the south,
together, you'd probably rub your eyes and look
again. At first you might think you were looking at
the relatives of some of the animals back home. A few
of them are, but most of them you'll find only in
Australia.

Among the crowd certainly you'd notice first a
big fellow with sharp-pointed, perked-up ears, standing on his hind legs and using his tail for a prop. If
a man six feet tall stood beside this animal he'd look
small. This animal's short front legs look so helpless
you'd wonder why Mother Nature bothered to put
them there at all.

If you were a stamp collector you'd know at once that this animal is a kangaroo. Australia has chosen him as her native animal because he was the animal best known to the early settlers.

When this great big, fur-covered animal was born he was a blind, naked little thing no more than an inch long and not at all able to care for himself. So he crawled into a soft, fur-lined pocket on his mother's breast and lived there for more than a month. He was even too helpless to nurse, so his mother had to force the milk into his mouth. When he was old enough to stick out his head he and his mother ate the leaves of the eucalyptus tree.

Pretty soon the little kangaroo was able to leave his mother's pocket and run about and play. But at the first sign of danger or when he got tired playing he would come back to his mother and hide or rest in her pocket.

The Australian people have nicknamed the kangaroo, *roo*. The father roo is called a buck, the mother a doe. You might think from the look of his soft brown eyes and from his good nature that this big fellow can be imposed upon. But, no, when he gets angry he can defend himself very well with his hind legs.

He knows exactly how to deal with unfriendly dogs. When a dog chases him he will back up against a tree and wait for the dog to come at him. Then, with the two front legs that look so small and helpless he will grab the dog. Up comes a hind foot with a toe nail as sharp as a knife and the first thing you know the dog will be killed.

Sometimes the roo will let the dog chase him to a stream of water where he jumps in, and wades out up to his neck. When the dog gets within reaching distance Mr. Roo's front paws will push the dog's head under the water and hold it there until he is drowned.

Mrs. Roo is not a fighter but she has ways of protecting her baby. Sometimes as she feels a hunter almost catching up with her she will throw the baby to one side in the bush and attract the hunter's attention by hopping off in another direction.

The kangaroo family eats leaves and plants and sometimes roots. Sometimes, too, they get into a farmer's sheep pasture and then a big hunt for the kangaroo follows. They are such grass eaters that if they stay long in a pasture there is no grass left for the sheep.

When the farmer chases kangaroos from his pasture he must run them along the fences. If he chases them toward a fence the animals will jump it as easily as you jump over a log. A four-foot fence means nothing to an animal that can leap thirty feet.

The kangaroo is hunted not only because he is a nuisance to the farmer, but the black natives like to eat his meat. And his hide makes a nice soft leather. So hunting the big roos which travel in herds in open country is one of Australia's sports. The roos give hunters lots of excitement because the high-powered creatures can take off faster than a horse and outrun him for quite some distance.

The koala is the most lovable little animal in the world. The idea of the toy Teddy Bear must have come from him because he is so soft and brown and cuddly. He has a sunny disposition, too. He seems to love people as much as people love him. He is just as happy being some one's pet as he is in his home in the top of a eucalyptus tree.

But it is impossible for any child outside of Australia to have a koala to love and play with, for the little fellow eats only the leaves of certain eucalyptus trees. And they grow only in Australia. Of the four hundred kinds of eucalyptus there are only twelve that the koala can safely eat. He likes sweets and will eat all you offer. But such food does not agree with him and he will die of indigestion if you let him have it.

The only water the koala needs he gets from the tree leaves. That is how he gets his name, for koala means "I do not drink." The koala is only an inch long when he is born. But the joey, as the baby is called, creeps into his mother's pouch to stay until he is about five inches long. Then he rides on his mothers' back until he can get around by himself. The koala never grows larger than two feet long and about a foot high. When he gets in trouble or thinks he is, he cries just like a human baby.

One man attempted to catch a koala he saw climbing the trunk of a eucalyptus tree. The tree was too slender for him to climb so he began cutting. The little bear scampered to the top branch and watched for a while.

All of a sudden he realized he was in danger. He threw his paws around the trunk of the tree as if it were his mother and started to cry. The harder the axe hit the harder the little fellow yelled. When the tree fell, the man ran to the koala and found his little paws still holding on for dear life. He didn't try to get away, but crept into the man's arms and lay like a contented baby.

So many ladies have wanted coats made from their lovely fur that there are hardly ten thousand of the little bears left in all the continent. But they are now being protected and each capital city has a bear farm where the koalas are cared for and at the same time are an attraction to visitors who go there to pet them.

Unlike the koala, the dingo has no friends. He is a sort of wild dog. Everybody hates him. He kills other animals for the fun of it. Early in the morning he jumps the fence of a sheep pasture and attacks the sheep. Sometimes he will kill as many as a dozen. Then he will eat part of one dead sheep, perhaps, and leave the rest lying there.

He's a coward for he always picks on timid animals. There are millions of sheep raised in Australia so the dingo has lots of his wicked fun. Like all criminals, he thinks he knows ways of escaping punishment.

He understands so well the ways of hunters and traps that it is hard to catch him that way. Poisoned bait seems to be the best way to get rid of a dingo. But you must be very careful in fixing it. His sense of smell tells him at once if the bait has been touched by a human being. If it has he won't go near it. There is nothing about the dingo to recommend him and it keeps the farmers of Australia busy thinking up new ways of getting rid of him. My, but they hate the dingo!

Australia's national bird is the emu. You will see it and the kangaroo on the country's coat of arms. The emu is a running bird like the ostrich and just about as big. He doesn't fight unless he has to, but when cornered, he fights with a two-way kick, sideways as well as backward. And a kick from one of his three-toed feet is enough to break a man's leg. The emu's feathers look more like hair than feathers.

The emu is very curious. He just has to find out what everything's all about. That makes him an easy target for the hunter because he will stop to find out about everything he sees or hears.

The emu's nest is a scooped-out place in the ground where the hen lays as many as thirteen eggs. During the day they leave them uncovered, but at night mama and papa emu take turns sitting on them. They never go very far from the nest at any time.

Another running, kicking bird is the cassowary. He will fight any creature—man, bird, or animal. He has little sense, just about enough to scratch around for bugs and insects or fruits and berries that have fallen on the ground. Even though he is stupid he is a popular bird, not for his looks but for his thick hide. It makes good strong rugs.

Of all Australia's birds one of the most interesting is the lyre bird. It has that name because the tail of the male bird is shaped like an ancient musical instrument called the lyre. This fellow likes to show off. When he can get one or two hens to listen, he finds a low pile of earth to use for a stage and then entertains them.

First, he spreads his beautiful tail feathers, then dances, sings, does imitations, from the laugh of the kockaburra to a train whistle. These birds live deep in the forest among ferns that grow as big as trees.

Long ago some one in Australia discovered what looked like a playhouse that might have been made by native children. But later it was found to be a room or bower made by the lyre bird. They make their nests in trees and the bower on the ground is where they play and entertain guests.

The male bird builds the bower of grasses and hunts all kinds of bright and shining things, like shells or seeds or buttons, to decorate the entrance. Some bower birds even put fresh flowers on the bower every day.

One naturalist often watched them as they danced, played hide and seek, and bowed to their sweethearts. If a visiting male showed bad manners the master of the bower was ready to fight. If the visitor moved as much as one flower the fight would be on before you could say "Jack Robinson."

Bats are the pest of the Australian fruit grower. At night they fly to the orchards and take their pick of peaches, plums, and pears. They sometimes fly in such large flocks that they knock off a good deal of the ripe fruit.

Even the earthworms of Australia are not all like earthworms in other parts of the world. Some grow from four to six feet long. Some even eleven feet long have been found. One worm like that would make fishing bait for a whole village of boys.

There are lizards without legs. One of them is called the slowworm. It is about two feet long and very brittle. When you hold it back of the head it snaps into several pieces.

In the waters around the tropical part of Australia you will see turtles large enough to ride on. The mother turtle goes to the shore to lay her eggs. She buries them about two feet deep in the sand. If you'd dig down in the sand you'd think at first that you had found a pile of tennis balls, but it would be about two hundred turtle eggs.

The natives hunt the eggs. They find a nest by poking in the sand with spears or sticks. If the point of the spear or stick comes up with a stain on it they know they have struck a turtle's nest. They like to eat them raw.

The warm sand hatches the baby turtles and right away they begin to push their way up. No sooner do they come to the surface than off they go making tracks for the sea. These three-inch long babies know exactly where they belong.

How would you like to sail to this island continent where Mother Nature keeps a zoo of such unusual animals?

—*Caroline H. Ridgway.*

Test and Study Exercises

1. Copy the sentence that best tells the main thought of this selection.

In Australia there are many animals strange to us.

The baby kangaroo is very small.

Farmers do not like the dingo.

The natives eat turtle eggs.

2. What is the Australian nickname of the kangaroo?

3. Does the koala have a pleasant disposition?

4. What is the greatest harm that the dingo does?

5. If you have ever seen any of the animals told about here, be ready to tell the class about them.

EMOTION

SENTIMENT and FUN

The Violet

PREPARATORY NOTE: Sometimes we do not know how important little things are. A story like this helps us appreciate them.

Many and many years ago, deep in the shadow of the dark green wood, there grew a violet. When the warm days of May came on she would unfold her hood of purple and greet with a smiling face the narrow shafts of sunlight which shot now and again through the branches of the old oak tree at the foot of which she grew.

Night after night she was lulled to sleep by the tinkle of the little brook as it danced and rippled onward through wood and through meadow on its long journey to the sea. Morning after morning she was awakened by the song of the birds as they peered at her between the leaves and sang to her of the great world outside the wood.

And so the summer came and went and the cold winds of coming winter moaned through the tree-tops. When the birds bade her good-by and flew away toward the sunny South, and the soft white snow fell quietly upon her, and the Frost King shut in the song of the brook, she dug her roots more firmly down into the rich warm earth, and lay dreaming of the time when her good friend, the South Wind, should again awaken her, and the birds and the brook should again tell her of the great things which they had seen far beyond the boundary of the dim and silent wood. And so as time went on she grew strong, and with her strength she grew more beautiful.

The robin sang to her of the lovely cherry blossoms and of the old apple tree, all in white, where she had built her nest. The saucy wren sang to her of green fields with nodding buttercups and of the rocky glen where the wild rose trailed over the stones. These were beautiful, he said, but they were as nothing compared to her own beautiful hues. And the little brown-breasted sparrow whispered to her of the sick child who caressed and kissed the bunch of purple blossoms which its mother had placed in its fever-stricken fingers. And the modest woodland violet heard all these things and deep down in her heart she longed to take part in the joys and sorrows of the outside world.

At last there came a time when the seasons seemed to change the order of their coming. The winds of March were hot, like those of the great Sahara; the showers of April refused to fall, or were drunk up in an instant by the waiting earth; the sun of May

burned and withered like that of August; the springs
dried up and all the flowers of the field withered and
died. But through all this sad time the woodland
violet, protected by the shadow of the gray old oak
and cooled by crystal water from the little brook,
flourished and grew strong as of old and again put
on her glorious attire to which she had added hundreds of beautiful blossoms.

One day a fisherman walked along the bank of
the little stream. He was an old man and from his
appearance it would seem that he cared but little
for the sport in which he was engaged, which was
true. He wandered apart and alone, filled with a
great sorrow. His best friend, a man among men,
a hero to all the earth for his deeds of charity and
good will, lay dead—and the whole world mourned.
As the fisherman reached the oak he cast aside his
tackle and throwing himself down upon the ground
he wept as only a strong man can weep in his grief.
Then his eyes caught sight of the purple garden at
his feet and through his tears there came a smile;
"They were his favorites," he whispered, and he
gathered the flowers, down to the tiniest bud, and
went his way.

Next day the hero lay in state in the marble halls
of the Capitol and a mighty throng passed in review
before all that remained of their leader and friend;
but one and all marvelled at the wondrous beauty
of the bunch of violets which lay upon the hero's
heart.

That night the birds and the brook told the story
of the honored place attained by the woodland violet,

and all said, "It is always so; to him who waits and hopes, allowing no discouragement to dim the beauty of his soul or the pride of his strength, there comes the greatest of all things at the last."

—*Charles Kimball.*

Test and Study Exercises

1. Where did the violet grow?

2. Why was the fisherman sad?

3. What happened to the brook in winter?

4. Why did the fisherman pick the violets?

5. Which part do you think contains the most beautiful thought in the story? Why do you think it is the most beautiful?

Suggested Activity

Be able to express the meaning of this sentence in your own words.

And the modest violet heard all these things and deep down in her heart she longed to take part in the joys and sorrows of the outside world.

Eletelephony

PREPARATORY NOTE: Read this little poem aloud to see how funny the words sound.

Once there was an elephant,
Who tried to use the telephant—
No! no! I mean an elephone
Who tried to use the telephone—
(Dear me! I am not certain quite
That even now I've got it right.)
Howe'er it was, he got his trunk
Entangled in the telephunk;
The more he tried to get it free,
The louder buzzed the telephee—
(I fear I'd better drop the song
Of elephop and telephong!)
—*Laura Richards.*

The Choice

PREPARATORY NOTE: Suppose that you had saved your money for a long time to buy something you wanted. Then when your money was all saved, you learned that a good friend of yours needed something badly. He needed it in order to live. What you wanted was something to have fun with. Should you buy what you had saved for? Or should you help your friend? Read to find out how the children in this story answered these questions.

The Two Families

It was the week before Christmas. The country folk for miles around could be seen, by foot and by wagon, streaming to the city, to make their purchases for the coming festivities. Even old Mrs. Rivers pushed steadily along and paid little attention to the heavy cans of milk which she carried.

Her mind was very busy thinking of the many places where she must deliver her milk; for the days preceding Christmas always brought double and triple the customary demand for milk and eggs, and it needed much thought on her part to carry out the orders.

Besides, she too had to stop at the city store, in order to purchase a gift for Paul, her orphaned grandson. This had to be not merely pretty but useful. She had no money to waste, for she was poor and had to earn her own living. But Paul was her joy and pride, and she worked willingly to support him. Besides Paul, she had another cherished possession, a treasure over which she rejoiced daily; and that was Bess, her cow, the like of which she had never seen.

Bess was a beautiful creature, with jet black hair which fairly sparkled on a sunshiny day. On her forehead there was a white spot, like a star. She was the happiest cow in the world, Paul and his grandmother believed. She was eight years old, just the same age as Paul, who really thought that he and Bess had the same birthday. Consequently, she always received on that memorable day a double portion of hay. Bess gave the best milk and plenty of it, so that some of it could be sold. Thus Paul and his grandmother owed part of their support to dear Bess.

During the summer months, Paul led Bess out into the flowery meadows, and it would have been difficult to decide which of the two enjoyed life better. At any rate they were the best of companions.

Mrs. Rivers had now filled all her orders, but she had not yet bought Paul's present. She stepped up to the window of a toy shop where were displayed such beautiful things as dolls, soldiers, sheep, goats, locomotives, steamboats and many other toys. But the most wonderful of all was a miniature castle, the tower of which held an instrument that gave forth music whenever a coin was dropped into it. This castle was a little savings bank, and at the same time a toy which coaxed for savings with its beautiful melodies. That just suited Mrs. Rivers' idea. "But," thought she doubtfully, "perhaps it is too expensive."

Surely there was nothing in that window cheap enough for her Paul. She was about to go, when an elegant carriage drawn by two beautiful horses neared the curb. She recognized the carriage at once, for it belonged to her landlord. While she stood gazing, the white-haired gentleman, enveloped in a big fur-lined coat, stepped out and entered the shop.

"He is going to buy some gifts for his grandchildren," thought she. "If I were rich like him, the giving of gifts would be my greatest pleasure."

Mrs. Rivers waited a moment longer at the window, for she was curious to know what the old man would buy. He examined many things, chose several toys, but still looked searchingly about for more. At last the salesman brought him the wonderful bank, and put a coin in the slot. All at once both men laughed, for just then the bank began to play. The old man was pleased, nodded with satisfaction, and the bank was added to his other purchases.

Mrs. Rivers sighed and went on. "I am sure a bank would be a nice present for Paul, too; sometimes I could put a few pennies into it, and I know it would please him. I'll just run over to the booths; there I'll be sure to get something cheap." At last, she spied something on the counter of the second booth, a toy made of tin and fashioned like a little house. It had a red roof, green shutters, and a little door with a key in the lock. A slot in the roof admitted the money, while the key unlocked the door, when one wished to count the contents.

"Fifty cents is a considerable amount for me to pay," thought she, "but for such a pretty toy, it is not too much." She drew out her purse and paid the money. Now she had something that all the bystanders praised, and naturally the merchant did the same.

Great joy filled the little cottage when Paul received his gift on Christmas morning. He leaped about, kissed and hugged his grandmother and then ran to the stall to Bess to show it to her. She, too, had received her gift, a whole bag of sweet-smelling clover. She had finished her meal, and was in a contented mood, eager to give a ready ear to Paul. She listened and uttered a couple of moo! moo's! She opened her eyes wide and gazed at the red and green colors of the bank. Probably she mistook it for a nice morsel and was about to lick it, when Paul shouted: "Oh no, Bess, that won't do"; and quickly put his bank behind his back. The cow just shook her head as much as to say: "If it's no good to eat, why do you show it to me?"

Paul forgave her for her stupidity, but he felt that he must let her know all about it, so he whispered into her ear: "That is a bank, and what is inside is fifteen pennies, and when I have more, I'm going to buy something nice."

Bess only nodded her head.

Paul understood her questioning look, and all at once he hugged the cow and said: "I know what I'm going to buy. I'm saving for you. You shall have a collar and a bell. Are you glad?"

Of course Bess was delighted, for it was no little matter, this promise of Paul's. Bess had often turned to look at the Baron's cow with her tinkling bell, and now she had hopes of soon wearing one herself.

Paul stroked Bess a few times, but he was getting uneasy and had to hasten to grandmother to tell her about his plans. So he said good-by to Bess and hurried to the house.

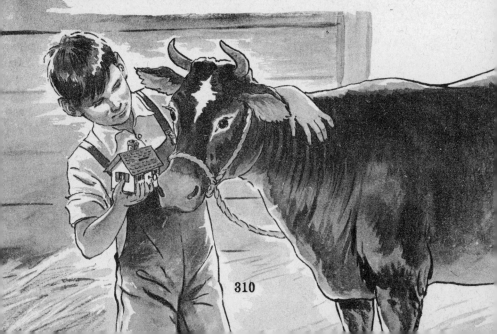

"Do you know what I'm going to do, grandmother?" cried Paul joyfully as he entered. "I'm going to save and buy Bess the finest bell in town."

"It will take you a long time to save so much money."

"Never mind," said Paul, "some day I'll have enough, even if it costs twenty-five dollars."

"Don't talk so silly," said his grandmother; "it certainly is time for you to go to school, in order to learn how much twenty-five dollars means. A bell like that is very expensive for such poor people as we are."

Paul felt sad. "I promised it to Bess. What will she think of me when she hears that I can't keep my word?" asked Paul.

"Don't fret," said his grandmother. "Even if it does cost a good deal, Bess deserves it. She supports us, so go ahead and save; and I will get the bell, when you have enough money."

This made Paul happy once more. He locked the door of the bank, and rejoiced over the fifteen pennies which made such a fine beginning.

Over in the landlord's house a brilliantly lighted Christmas tree reached from the floor to the ceiling of the grand drawing room which was filled with a merry party. Upon the long table lay the many gifts, for big and little folks; and each one had received just the present wished for, and many more things besides.

The children had been so surprised with their gifts, that not until now had they begun to examine them closely. Everything was beautiful, but they liked that present which grandfather had bought for them all, and that was the bank.

It played beautifully, but it wouldn't play for nothing. So kind grandfather had brought a number of coins to be dropped into the bank.

Bob and Fred took turns putting in coins; and little Elsie wouldn't have had a chance if her mother hadn't demanded a turn for her.

"That's enough, my children," said the father, "the coins that grandfather brought are almost all gone, and if you keep on at this rate, you'll have none for tomorrow."

The children looked at one another disappointed; but Fred had a clever idea. "We'll ask grandfather for more," said he.

"I don't think I bargained for that," said the grandfather. "Save ahead of time, and you'll have something when you need it. So be careful of the coins, for I don't intend to feed your bank forever."

"That's too bad," thought Bob.

"You must save for yourselves," said the grandfather.

"Just do your work at school and at home," said the father, "and you know I will keep up your weekly allowance."

Bob and Fred had now been at school for a year or more, and their desire to learn had not always been very keen, and their record not of the best.

"I don't go to school," murmured Elsie, "and it will be a long while before I earn anything."

"Well, I know a little girl that soils her clothes much too quickly, and who doesn't wash her hands

often enough, and who does not keep her toys orderly," said the mother.

"I'm that girl, I know," said Elsie, ashamed.

"If you would do your work better, I would give you a small allowance every Saturday night," said the mother, smilingly.

"Oh, I'll try," shouted Elsie gleefully.

"I should like to know what you'll do with all the money that you save?" questioned grandfather.

"We could go to the confectioner's and buy everything nice to eat, couldn't we, Elsie?" cried Bob.

"But," said Fred, "then all our money would be gone and we should have nothing to show for it."

"Now I'll tell why I bought the bank," said the grandfather. "I wanted you to learn how long it takes to save a little money. That it takes one hundred pennies before you have a dollar. Then, besides, I thought you could buy something nice for your money, and learn at the same time how hard it is and how long it takes before one can get what he wants. So far, you have just asked for things, and your parents have given them to you."

The children had listened carefully, and now agreed to the idea. But the burning question was: "What shall we buy with the money?"

Elsie timidly said that chocolate would be her choice, but the boys laughed at that and her mother had to soothe her little girl's wounded feelings.

The two boys wanted a little cannon that they could fire off on special days, but Elsie shuddered at the thought, while their mother said they could not have such a dangerous toy.

It was a difficult problem. Ideas were suggested and turned down, till at last Bob cried: "I have it, I have it. We'll buy a goat and a cart and drive about."

This met the approval of all, but Fred suggested two goats as being better able to pull a load of three. This was satisfactory.

"Then," continued Bob, "let's have a cover on the wagon so that we can drive in rainy weather. I'll sit in front and drive; it won't matter if I do get wet a little. You and Elsie can sit inside—and Fred, you pretend that you're grandfather."

"No, you can do that," said Fred quickly, "I'd rather be the driver."

"No, I had better drive," said Bob, "for you know, Fred, that you always get a cold so easily."

"I don't care a bit about that. I'm the eldest and have the first right."

"That's why I said you should be grandfather. He's old," said Bob.

This disputing might have gone on endlessly, if grandfather had not said that the only way to settle the trouble was that they should take turns.

It didn't take them very long to discover that the saving of pennies was a very slow process. They did not always do their school and home work well and did not always earn their allowances. Elsie, too, often fell short on account of carelessness in her habits of cleanliness. So the amount of money increased slowly, and the goats and the wagon for which they all yearned were still far, far off.

Thus the winter passed, and although the children had enjoyed the snow which brought sleighing and skiing, still they rejoiced at the return of spring. After school hours they could be found in the garden or strolling through the fields and woods.

They often met Paul leading Bess, and they asked him how he spent the winter, as they stood patting the gentle cow.

Without waiting to hear Paul's answer, Bob said: "How nice your cow looks. Does she still give much milk?"

"I should say so," Paul answered with pride. "We make quite a little money, because all the people like her milk and come to us to buy it."

"You like your cow, don't you?" asked Bob.

Paul agreed with a quick nod. "First I like my grandmother, and then Bess comes second. Bess likes me, too. Don't you, you good old cow?"

Bess knew that an answer was expected and murmured a little and nosed at the plant Paul had in his hand, but he pulled it away quickly.

"That isn't for you, Bess," cried Paul, "and yet it is, too."

Bess couldn't understand such contradictory language, and the children couldn't, either. So they asked Paul to explain.

"Well, this is how it is. My grandmother takes the plants I gather, and sells them to the druggist; and the money that she gets for them she puts into my bank."

"Have you a bank?" interrupted the children. "What is it like? Does it make music? Is it pretty?"

To this last question Paul answered, "Yes," with great certainty. Then he described his bank and they told about theirs.

"Have you money in your bank?" asked Elsie.

"I'll soon have a dollar," said Paul proudly: "only seventy-five cents are missing. My grandmother gave me fifteen pennies for Christmas, and they look like gold. Since then she has given me a penny as often as she could."

"We are going to buy a cart and two goats to pull it, when we have enough money. What are you going to buy?"

Paul looked at Bess and laughed. "It's something for her," said he. "It's going to be a pretty collar and a nice bright bell, because she deserves it."

The children agreed and gazed at the cow respectfully. They believed her to be an extraordinary animal, and they fully wished her to have such a pretty ornament as Paul had described.

The friendship between these children grew closer each day; they met often and Paul took Bess with him whenever he went, for while she grazed he sought for plants.

One day the children brought their banks with them, for it was absolutely necessary to compare them. The brothers had kept two coins safely in their pockets, and now they dropped one into the slot before the astonished eyes of their friend. Paul then shook his bank, opened the door with the key, and let the children look at his riches. They were now thoroughly satisfied and hopeful.

Paul's money had increased but slowly; for his grandmother was very poor, the druggist didn't pay well, and Paul couldn't always find just the plants that were needed. But still Paul rejoiced over every penny that brought him one step nearer to his hopes; and Bob and Fred often helped Paul gather the plants, for they were anxious that he should get on also.

Elsie gathered the flowers that seemed the most fragrant to her and brought them to Paul, even though they could not be used by the druggist; still

she believed that she was doing her share of work. Thus the summer months sped by all too quickly.

With dread the children saw the winter approaching, for that meant that they would see less of one another, "But never mind," they would say, "when we get our goats, we can drive anywhere and visit you, Paul."

"Yes, and you'll be able to hear my Bess' bell ring from the distance," said Paul gaily.

"It will sound so nice and we'll just follow the sound," said Bob.

"Then we'll meet and we'll step out of our cart and let Bess and the goats graze, while we gather plants for the druggist, so that you can get some money in your bank to buy something else."

"But what shall we save for next?" asked Elsie.

That certainly was not an easy question to answer. It gave rise to much talk and before it was decided, the weather grew cold and caused the beginning of a long separation. Only now and then did they meet on the sliding pond; and soon Paul did not come at all. Then the children learned that he had to take care of his grandmother, who had broken her leg in a fall on the ice.

Making the Choice

Paul had to make the fires, cook the meals, clean house, mind Bess; and all in all it was more than his strength would permit. Once in a while a kind-hearted neighbor helped him, and another woman who pitied brave Mrs. Rivers often sent her food.

Sometimes the rich children brought some food, too, for they wanted to visit Paul, their best friend, and they were given permission. Fred carried the soup; Bob, the meat; and Elsie, the fruit. What a joy it was for them to do this. They never stayed long, however, for the room was so little and so dark that they felt unhappy and uncomfortable in it. Besides, Paul didn't seem natural to them in his little house, as he did in the big fields. Not until he took them to the stall to visit Bess did any one of them appear natural.

"Will your grandmother's leg get mended?" asked Elsie, for she really thought that the broken leg was lying about in little pieces.

"Oh, yes, the doctor says it will," answered Paul, "but my grandmother can never again deliver milk. That is certain."

"Then she can't earn any money," said Fred.

"We'll get along, I think, for we still have Bess, and she helps with her milk."

So for the time all cares were laid by, and the children returned to their home.

At last spring came again. After dark dreary days, storms and rains, the sun shone brightly all day. The green grass and delicate flowers came out of their winter beds. Now Paul could go out again with Bess, and indeed he needed it after his hard, trying winter. Mrs. Rivers, still weak, was able to go about a little, but she had to use a cane. It almost seemed as if Bess understood and was trying to help, for never had she given so much milk, and such rich milk, too.

The children again met in the fields, greeted one another, and petted Bess. What didn't they have to tell about everything that had happened during the months of their separation!

"It won't take much longer now," said Fred, "and we'll have our goats. When we were in town lately with our father we selected the cart."

"It's beautiful," cried Bob, "but it cost a great deal of money."

"Just one more gold coin and we'll have the goats," said Fred, "and then we'll drive like princes."

"Bess must have her bell, too, so that we can find you quickly," said Elsie.

Paul hesitated. The boys noticed that something was wrong.

"You didn't change your mind, Paul, did you? Shall Bess have no bell?" asked Bob.

Paul shook his head.

"I think that's mean of you," cried Fred angrily.

"If I were Bess, I shouldn't like you another minute," said Bob. "Yes, you're a nice boy. First you promise Bess a bell and tell her every day how beautiful she'll look. Then, when she's really pleased, she's to be disappointed, and must walk about like any old cow."

"You poor Bess," said Elsie sadly, and then looked at Paul scornfully.

He controlled his feelings like a man, but his lips quivered as he said: "I couldn't help it, and I explained to Bess why she can't have the bell."

"Oh, those are just excuses," cried Fred.

"You're a miser," said Bob.

"No, I'm not that," said Paul, in defense of his actions. "I love my Bess so much that I can't tell how much, but I love my grandmother still more. She was so sick and so weak, and needed medicine. How could I get it without money? So I took my key, unlocked my bank and used the money to buy fruit and other things for her."

"Did the fruit help her?" asked Elsie.

"Oh yes," said Paul, "but it's all gone now. The doctor says it helped her like medicine."

"Do you know, I think Bess is prettier without a collar and bell," said Bob.

"I, too, like her much better this way," said Elsie.

"Who knows if the ringing of the bell might not have frightened Bess," added Fred.

After they had tried to comfort Paul, they left him, and at once began a race to see who could reach home first to tell everything they had just learned about poor Paul.

The father listened with interest to their suggestions and sent his servant to bring out two baskets of fruit. Now a quarrel arose as to who should carry the baskets to Mrs. Rivers, and at last it was decided that each boy should carry one.

Elsie was sad and said softly: "I should have liked to carry something, too. I can go just as fast as the boys, and I like Paul just as much as they do."

The mother was pleased with her little daughter's kindness, and gave her a jar of quince jelly to carry.

Mrs. Rivers thanked the children and their parents, and Paul hugged Bess for joy and said: "Now grandmother will surely get better."

Bess just nodded contentedly and Paul knew she agreed with him.

Two days later, Elsie's long looked-for birthday arrived, and under the cake with its six candles lay a much desired gold piece, which she at once put into the bank. Then the boys brought out their report from school and received their allowance, which they put into the bank. The bank had gained with great rapidity.

"Now it's time for us to buy the goats. The cart has been selected and as soon as we have the goats the man will deliver it," said the father.

But the goats were not so easily obtained. They must match in size and color; have big horns, and long beards, and nice dispositions. In short, there weren't two such goats to be found; so the children, although disappointed, at last agreed to wait till such goats could be obtained. The children hoped on, and each night went to bed expecting to see the goats in the morning.

At last word was received that two goats of the required description had been found; but it still remained to be seen whether they would be unruly or whether the children could manage them.

"Paul must see the goats, too," shouted the children. "Too bad he can't bring Bess up here. Oh well, Bess will soon get acquainted with the goats, and be a good friend of theirs."

"I wonder where Paul is today? I didn't see him on the road—maybe he took Bess to the woods." But Paul was nowhere to be found; and so the children decided to run down to his house and find out.

But my, what a difference there was between their joy and Paul's sorrow. On the table stood his dinner untouched. The room was empty. In the stable they found Paul and his grandmother bending over Bess, who seemed in great pain and very sick, indeed. The old woman had her head hidden in her apron, and Paul sat beside his Bess holding the nicest hay before her lips without her taking the slightest notice of his efforts.

Shocked and tearful, the children looked at the sad picture.

"What ails Bess?" cried Bob.

"We don't know," answered Paul, who had no friendly greeting for his playmates today. "We found her sick this morning."

Elsie took Paul's hand, as her tears streamed down her sad face, while Bob said: "Perhaps she's eaten something that wasn't good for her—but she'll get better."

But Mrs. Rivers shook her head and said: "No, Bess has eaten something that has poisoned her. When the doctor was here this morning, he said that he couldn't save her."

The children forgot all about their goats and only thought about poor Bess. Dumbfounded they stood and looked at the misery. They couldn't give help or comfort, so they slipped away and ran home to get help there.

The head stableman was sent down to examine Bess, but he said there was nothing to be done. That was a sad day for Paul and his grandmother and even for the children. They hastened down in the morning to see Paul.

"Don't cry," said they. "Bess was a beautiful cow, but there are more cows."

"Not for me," said Paul. "We can never buy another. Bess helped to support us. Now maybe we'll have to move because we can't pay the rent." He cried in grief, and the children cried too. Again they felt their helplessness to cheer Paul, so one by one they ran off.

"Hurry, Elsie," cried Bob, "we have no time to wait for you, we must hurry and tell Father to give Paul another cow."

Their father listened to them and felt very sad that such a blow had come to these poor people his children liked.

"You'll send them another cow, won't you?" asked Fred.

"A real nice one, the best one you can get?" pleaded Elsie.

The father looked at his children and said: "No, I can't do that. I'm not so rich that I can give a cow to every poor person who happens to lose one. We, too, live from our cows and the products of our land. I must pay for the expense of the house, for you and your mother and myself; and what I have left over, I must share with many poor people. A cow is expensive and I cannot give such a present."

The children felt sad, for the picture of the dead cow, the poor woman and the weeping boy, would not leave their minds.

The next afternoon the goats were harnessed to the cart and brought up to the house to be tested; and everyone was sure that now the children would once more be happy. Everything went off beautifully. The dealer had not praised his goats too much. They were full of fire and one couldn't have selected a finer team.

But, however fine the display had been, the children didn't seem to care much about the goats, even though they did attract their attention for a minute or two. Their thoughts always returned to Paul and his poor Bess.

"Oh, if the goats would only turn into a cow," sighed Elsie.

"Wouldn't it be nice," cried Fred. "Then we could milk her and give the milk to Paul and his grandmother to sell."

"But you can't drive around town with a cow," said Bob.

"If I could make Bess alive again, I shouldn't care about driving around town," said Fred.

"But you can't do that," said Bob, sighing.

"I suppose there are cows almost as nice as Bess. Don't you think so?" asked Elsie.

Those words made the boys think. First they said nothing, then they looked at each other, and suddenly they shouted in one voice: "We'll buy a cow instead of the goats. Do you agree with us, Elsie?"

"Of course I do. How fine, how grand!"

"It was you who first gave us the thought," said the boys, giving their sister the full share of the honor.

"If father will only agree with us," said Fred, thoughtfully.

"He will," said Bob, hopefully. "Let us hurry to tell him."

Like wild deer they fled to the house, so that their grandfather called out to them, "Is anything on fire?"

"Oh, we have something to ask father." When they reached the house Bob shouted: "Don't be angry with us, father—only listen to us, please. We should like to buy a cow for Paul. May we?"

"With what?" asked the father, in surprise.

"With the money in our bank," cried the children.

"Then you can't have any goats or wagon, for a cow is expensive, and it will take all your money."

"That doesn't matter; we'll begin to save all over again," the children assured him. "First let us give the cow to Paul."

"Beginning all over again will be a slow work," said the grandfather. "Before you again have money for goats, you'll be too old for such sport."

The children looked at one another, and a shade of sadness passed over their faces. For years they had wished for goats, many a night they had dreamed about them, and now nothing was to come of it all. "Think it over well, before it's too late," said the father. "Now you're filled with pity for Paul; but afterward you'll pity yourselves over your own loss."

The children's hesitation lasted but a moment and they decided without consulting one another, for they read the answer in one another's eyes, and they shouted: "Oh, no, we don't want the goats, we'd rather buy a cow; and you must help us, Father, to get one just like Bess."

"Well, if you are so set upon it, you must have your way," responded the father, highly pleased. "We must ask the overseer to help us."

The directions were given to this man. A very exact description of Bess was sent with the order. But it was no easy matter to find a cow that had so many good qualities.

Meanwhile the dealer again came with the goats and praised them and tested and showed all their good points, but it made no difference to the children —all they wanted was the cow.

"Well, then," said he, "I will sell the goats to the man in the next house. He has children and I'm sure he wants something nice for them. You'll be sorry when you see them driving and you must go on foot."

Now this was making the matter rather hard to bear. Bob and Fred never did like the boys in the next house, and the thought that they should possess the goats rather disturbed them. But—they weren't going to care, and so the dealer sold the goats and the wagon to the neighbor.

For Paul and his grandmother the days were passing slowly and sadly. The old grandmother could do but little; and no one seemed to have any work that Paul was old enough to do.

Paul had seen but little of his playmates. He felt that they had wiped him out of their thoughts, and it pained him. Thus a few days went by.

At last the overseer, who had searched very hard, found a cow which answered all requirements. Happily, her name was Bess. The children inspected the cow and were more than pleased with her, and the money was brought forth to pay for her. This was a glorious moment. Fred unlocked the bank, Elsie took out the money, and Bob counted it. Meanwhile the cow sent forth an occasional "moo" as if she were asking what they intended doing with her. But she was only tied to a tree for the present. There were many more things to be accomplished before she could go to her new home.

This cow had cost a big sum of money but not all that the bank held. Grandfather thought that the money left over could be used as a new beginning for the bank.

But the children didn't think so. The youngest cried: "Oh, no, we must buy a collar and a bell for the cow just as Paul always wished."

Bob and Fred both kissed Elsie for the thought and said that she always knew best.

The overseer told them that they had enough money for a collar and a bell and that some money would still be left.

"Then let us buy a milk pail," shouted Elsie.

So the overseer took the children to town to buy the extras, while Bess stood grazing in the meadow.

Such a day the children had never had in all their lives. When everything had been purchased to their entire satisfaction, they could scarcely sit still in the carriage until they reached home. When they finally arrived, they could not eat their supper for joy.

The cow was brought forward and the collar and bell were adjusted while the happy household watched and rejoiced with the children. Bess shook her head, and the tones from the bell were clear and sweet. She seemed to enjoy the sound. The stable boy now led Bess by a rope, the two boys walked on either side of the cow, each with a bundle of hay, and Elsie brought up the rear carrying the milk pail. Thus they marched till they reached the little cottage. Mrs.

Rivers was seated at the window trying to read, but her glasses were wet with tears and she couldn't see. Paul was trying to write, but a big tear had just blotted his page. Suddenly he heard a jingling, jangling, just like a cow bell, and an occasional "moo." It sounded to him just like his Bess.

He raised his eyes. There he saw at his door a cow with two bundles of hay at her side, and Elsie with a milk pail. What did it mean?

A cry of "Paul, Paul, where are you?" soon brought him to the door.

"Here's your cow, Bess," and just then she uttered "moo, moo." The children placed the rope in Paul's hand and said: "We have brought you a new cow and a pail and some hay."

Paul couldn't think how it all happened. Had Bess come back to life, or was he dreaming?

"Does Bess suit you? Isn't she pretty? We bought her with the money in our bank."

Paul nodded to all they said, for how could he answer when his heart was so full?

Now the cow was examined on all sides and every one agreed that such a beautiful cow could be found nowhere else in the world, for she was exactly like Bess. Then they admired the pail, and of course the collar and bell.

"The bell sounds just like the organ in the church," said Paul.

"Does the cow give milk?" asked the grandmother. At once she seated herself on the little stool beside the cow, and from under her hands streamed forth the white, foaming milk into the brand new milking pail, which was soon filled to overflowing. All this time Paul was hugging his new cow and was stroking her head, while she licked his other hand.

"Couldn't tell her from Bess," said he, and certainly he was the one to know. Then Paul and his grandmother kissed the children and thanked them for their wonderful kindness.

When the children reached home, they found their empty bank. They took it and petted it tenderly.

"It was a good bank," said Fred. "Such joy we never had before, and we must thank the bank."

"Yes, we must respect it; and I'm going to begin at once to save again."

"I, too," cried Elsie; "and when we have enough, let's give it to some poor people."

The brothers nodded and said: "That's what we'll do."

They were tired out now from their long day's excitement and went to bed and slept as they had never slept before.

Paul and his grandmother once more lived contentedly, supported by their second Bess, and their thanks to the children had no end.

The children were satisfied when they saw Bess and her master, Paul. When the neighbor's children drove by in the goat cart, and cried: "See, see, you have no goats," they didn't care.

They had acquired something far richer with their savings, "The Joy of Giving."

—*Anonymous.*

Test and Study Exercises

1. What do you think is the main thought of this story? Write your answer on your paper, and be ready to tell why you think so.

2. Be able to tell the meaning of each of these words that are used in the story.

possession	miniature	locomotives
creature	sparkled	displayed
satisfaction	purchases	expensive
rejoiced	murmured	difficult
compare	dreary	acquired
counter	landlord	coins

3. What was the name of Paul's grandmother?

4. What were the names of Paul's friends?

5. What did the children finally decide to do with their money?

6. What present did Paul receive on Christmas morning?

7. What were the other children saving their money for?

8. Which person in this story did you like best?

9. Choose the part of the story you liked best and be ready to read it to the class.

Suggested Activities

1. Make an outline that will show all the important things that happened in the part of the story called "The Two Families."

2. If you had to make a choice like the one in the story, do you think it would be hard? Be able to talk about this.

Through a Shop Window

PREPARATORY NOTE: As you read this poem, try to see in your mind what the word pictures describe.

How full the glittering shops are now
    With clattering tongues and open purses,
And children scrambling anyhow
    Beside their mothers, aunts, and nurses;
With eager eyes and laughing lips,
    And problems of a thousand choices,
With loaded trees, and lucky dips,
    And Christmastime in all the voices!
You scarce can push your way along
    Behind the window—which discloses
Outside the little ragged throng
    With longing eyes and flattened noses.
               —*Eleanor Farjeon.*

A Day with Dr. Good Speech

PREPARATORY NOTE: This little play is funny, but it also shows how some people learn to speak better. Perhaps you have some of the speech troubles that Dr. Good Speech takes care of. If your teacher wants your class to act out the play, be sure that you are able to read your part correctly.

CAST OF CHARACTERS

Dr. Good Speech, who speaks very well
Nurse Speakwell, the doctor's assistant
Paul, who uses words he doesn't need
Ted and Ned, twins, who fail to use their jaws, lips, and tongues when they talk
Betty Lou, whose grammar needs improving
Mrs. Bradley, Betty Lou's mother
Dick, who always substitutes *w* for *wh*
Tony, a child with foreign accent whose chief difficulty is with his *th's*
Jane, who is almost cured of her speech trouble, which was substituting short *i* for short *e*
Jerry, who also is almost well. Jerry substituted short *i* for short *u*

SCENE: *The office of* DR. GOOD SPEECH

TIME: *9 o'clock, Saturday morning*

(*As the play opens,* NURSE SPEAKWELL *is seated at her desk looking over the list of cases for the day.* DR. GOOD SPEECH *enters and the nurse rises.*)

335

Doctor. Good morning, Nurse Speakwell.

Nurse. Good morning, Dr. Good Speech.

Doctor. Are we going to be very busy today, nurse? Have you made many appointments for me?

Nurse (looking in the appointment book). Yes, Dr. Good Speech, there are several children coming in.

Doctor (taking off his suit coat and putting on his office coat). That is fine! I am always glad when I can help the children overcome their speech difficulties. Ah, here comes someone now.

(The first patient enters—a boy named PAUL.*)*

Nurse. Good morning, young man. How are you today? What trouble have you been having with your speech?

Paul. Why-uh . . . . my teacher-uh . . . . why-uh . . . . she-uh . . . . suggested I see Dr. Good Speech because . . . . uh she said I go and use so many words I don't need. She-uh . . . . said . . . .

Nurse. Dr. Good Speech, here is a patient whom you can help, I am sure.

Doctor. Your teacher is right, my boy. Just a minute and I shall give you a prescription that will help you get rid of your unnecessary words. *(The doctor writes instructions and hands the prescription to the patient.)*

Paul (reading aloud).

1. *Know what you are going to say.*
2. *Choose the right words.*
3. *Leave out all words you do not need.*

Doctor. In other words, Paul, think before you talk!

Paul. Thank you, Dr. Good Speech. I guess I do talk without thinking very much. I shall try to follow your advice, doctor. Thank you, and good-by.

Doctor. I hope you will soon improve. (*As* Paul *goes out, the twins,* Ned *and* Ted, *come in.*)

Nurse. Good morning, boys. You have been here before. You can tell the doctor what your speech defects are.

Ted. Our teacher says we do not open our jaws when we talk. . . .

Ned. Or use our tongues and our lips as we should.

Doctor. Well, boys, here are some exercises that will help you. Now stretch your tongues—both of you—and move them as far as you can in the way I tell you. *Up-in, up-in; down-in, down-in.* (*The twins follow directions and stretch their tongues up toward their noses and down to their chins.*) Now sweep your tongue along the roof of your mouth:

forward-back; backward-front. (*The twins follow instructions.*) That's fine. Now for the lip exercises. Move your lips so I can see them moving as you say, *ee-oo; ah-oo . . . . ee-oo; ah-oo.* (*The doctor instructs the boys who repeat the exercises after him.*) Practice these exercises several times each day and you'll soon see a difference. Come back to see me when your teacher thinks you speak more distinctly.

Ned. We appreciate your help, doctor.

Ted. And we'll practice every day. My lips move better already. (*As the twins leave the office, a lady with a little girl enters. It is* Mrs. Bradley *and* Betty Lou.)

Nurse. Good morning. Is this a new patient for Dr. Good Speech?

Mrs. Bradley. Yes. I phoned for an appointment. I am Mrs. Bradley and this is Betty Lou. (Nurse Speakwell *gets a card and makes a notation on it. She then hands the card to* Dr. Good Speech.)

Doctor. What is your trouble, Betty Lou?

Betty Lou. Always I say, "I ain't got none." I don't suppose you could help me correct that mistake.

Doctor. Oh, yes, Betty Lou. You really know better. But you need some practice in saying the correct form. Repeat after me three times: *I haven't any . . . . I haven't any . . . . I haven't any.* (*He writes those words on a card which he hands to* Betty Lou.)

Betty Lou. Thank you, Dr. Good Speech. I shall try very hard to do what you say.

Mrs. Bradley. Thank you for helping us, doctor.

Betty Lou. Good-by, Dr. Good Speech. (BETTY LOU *and her mother leave.* DICK *comes into the office.*)

Doctor. Hello, young man. What may I do for you today?

Dick. Will you help me with my *WH* sounds? Everyone tells me I sound a *w* instead of a *wh* in *w'en, w'at,* and *w'y.*

Doctor. Yes, Dick, I can see you do. But if you follow my directions, we'll soon change that. In making *wh* you really sound *h* and *w;* that is, you blow the *w* out with a little puff of air—just as if you were blowing out the candles on a birthday cake. If you want to test yourself, hold your hand in front of your face as you say *wh* or *hw.* (DICK *tries.*) What happens?

Dick. I feel the little puffs of air, doctor; and it's fun, too.

Doctor. If you want to compare what you were doing with the new and correct pronunciation of *wh,* here is a list for you. Pronounce these words aloud.

Dick. Wear .... where
were .... whir
weather .. whether
witch .... which
world .... whirled

They are just alike except for the beginning sound, aren't they, Dr. Good Speech? I believe I can help myself, now. Thank you very much, doctor. (*He leaves the office saying why, what, when, etc. He is so intent on his practice that he almost bumps into* TONY, *who is coming into the office.*)

Tony. Is dis de doctor's office?

Nurse. Of course it is, and this is Dr. Good Speech. (*The nurse introduces* TONY *to the doctor.*)

Tony. My name's Tony. All de boys laugh at me for saying *de, dem, dat,* an' *dose.* Is dis de place to get some help?

Doctor. The boys are right, Tony, but they shouldn't laugh. You do say *de* for *the,* and *dat* for *that;* but I have a cure for you. Make the *th* sound by placing the tip of your tongue between your teeth and blowing gently, like this: (*the doctor shows how it is done*) this, that, then. (TONY *tries; has trouble; tries again. The doctor turns to* NURSE SPEAKWELL.) Please prepare a list of *th* words for Tony, nurse.

Nurse (*writing a list*). Here they are, Tony. Let me hear you pronounce them.

Tony. *D*is . . . . *th*is (correcting himself) ; *the,* *th*at, *th*ese, *th*em, *th*ere.

Doctor. That is very good. Practice them at home, and come back to see me next Saturday. Good-by, Tony.

Tony. G'by, doc!

(JANE *and* JERRY *come in together, happily.*)

Jane. We've come back to show you how much our pronunciation has improved after practicing the words you gave us last week. Just listen to my short *e's.*

GET must rhyme with WET and PET.

Mother will *let* me *get* a dress.

Jerry. And my short *u's* are very good, too, I think.

JUST will always rhyme with MUST.

Just watch me catch the ball.

I couldn't say *just* when I started. At least, I *didn't* say *just*—but now I do!

Doctor. That is very fine. Come again if ever you have other speech problems. (JANE *and* JERRY *go out.*)

Nurse. That was the last appointment we had for today, doctor.

Doctor. Ho-hum, I'm tired. (*The doctor yawns and stretches.*) But it's worth the effort when one hears poor speech changing into such good speech. And what fun the children have!

Nurse (*clearing her desk*). That's right, Dr. Good Speech. And tomorrow will bring to the office other children you can help. Good-night, doctor.

Doctor. Good-night, Nurse Speakwell.

341

A Word Game

In playing this word game, be sure to pronounce all the words correctly. All the words come from the speech play you have just read.

Choose a word from one of the three columns and say, "I am thinking of a word in column ...."

Then the guessing begins.

In turn, each boy or girl in the class says, "Is the word ....?" You answer, "No, the word is not ....," or "Yes, the word is ...." Be sure you do not forget the word you have chosen.

The one who guesses the word which you chose is the next leader, and the guessing begins again.

1	2	3
characters	assistant	grammar
jaws	tongues	improving
foreign	difficulty	accent
cured	substituting	trouble
seated	children	patient
appointments	prescription	what
thinking	advice	follow
defects	forward	teacher
practice	hello	pronunciation
pronounce	beginning	except
again	Saturday	listen
that	get	problems

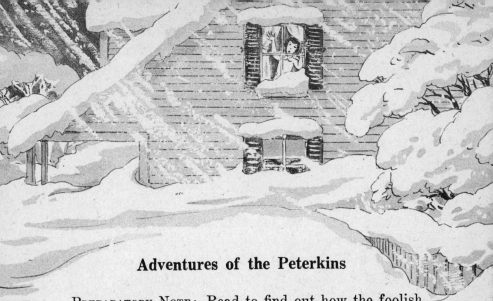

Adventures of the Peterkins

PREPARATORY NOTE: Read to find out how the foolish,
funny Peterkins in this story met their big problems.

The Peterkins Snowed Up

Mrs. Peterkin awoke one morning to find a heavy
snowstorm raging. The wind had swept the snow
against the windows, had heaped it up around the
house, and thrown it into huge white drifts.

Mrs. Peterkin went from one window to the other
to look out; but nothing could be seen but the driving
storm and the deep white snow. Even Mr. Brom-
wick's house, on the opposite side of the street, was
hidden by the swift-falling flakes.

"What shall I do about it?" thought Mrs. Peterkin.
"No roads cleared out! Of course there'll be no
butcher and no milkman!"

The first thing to be done was to wake up all the
family early; for there was enough in the house
for breakfast, and there was no knowing when they
would have anything more to eat.

So she went from one room to the other, as soon as it was light, waking the family, and before long all were dressed and downstairs. And then all went round the house to see what had happened.

All the water pipes in the house were frozen. The milk was frozen. They could open the door into the woodhouse; but the woodhouse door into the yard was banked up with snow; and the front door, and the piazza door, and the side door stuck. Nobody could get in or out!

Meanwhile, Amanda, the cook, had succeeded in making the kitchen fire, but had discovered there was no furnace coal.

"The furnace coal was to have come today," said Mrs. Peterkin, apologetically.

"Nothing will come today," said Mr. Peterkin, shivering.

But a fire could be made in the stove in the dining room.

All were glad to sit down to breakfast and hot coffee. The little boys were much pleased to have "ice cream" for breakfast.

"When we get a little warm," said Mr. Peterkin, "we will consider what is to be done."

"I am thankful I ordered the sausages yesterday," said Mrs. Peterkin. "I was to have had a leg of mutton today."

"Nothing will come today," said Agamemnon, gloomily.

"Are these sausages the last meat in the house?" asked Mr. Peterkin.

"Yes," said Mrs. Peterkin.

The potatoes also were gone, the barrel of apples empty, and she had meant to order more flour that very day.

"Then we are eating our last provisions," said Solomon John, helping himself to another sausage.

"I almost wish we had stayed in bed," said Agamemnon.

"I thought it best to make sure of our breakfast first," repeated Mrs. Peterkin.

"Shall we literally have nothing left to eat?" asked Mr. Peterkin.

"There's the pig!" suggested Solomon John.

Yes, happily, the pigsty was at the end of the wood-house, and could be reached under cover. But some of the family could not eat fresh pork.

"We should have to 'corn' part of him," said Agamemnon.

"My butcher has always told me," said Mrs. Peterkin, "that if I wanted a ham I must keep a pig. Now we have the pig, and have not the ham!"

"Perhaps we could 'corn' one or two of his legs," suggested one of the little boys.

"We need not settle that now," said Mr. Peterkin. "At least the pig will keep us from starving."

The little boys looked serious; they were fond of their pig.

"If we had only decided to keep a cow," said Mrs. Peterkin.

"Alas! yes," said Mr. Peterkin, "one learns a great many things too late!"

"Then we might have had ice cream all the time!" exclaimed the little boys.

Indeed, the little boys, in spite of the prospect of starving, were quite pleasantly excited at the idea of being snowed in, and hurried through their breakfast that they might go and try to shovel out a path from one of the doors.

"I ought to know more about the water pipes," said Mr. Peterkin. "Now, I shut off the water last night in the bathroom, or else I forgot to; and I ought to have shut it off in the cellar."

The little boys came back. Such a wind at the front door, they were going to try the side door.

"Another thing I have learned today," said Mr. Peterkin, "is not to have all the doors on one side of the house, because the storm blows the snow against all the doors."

Solomon John started up. "Let us see if we are blocked up on the east side of the house!" he exclaimed.

"Of what use," asked Mr. Peterkin, "since we have no door on the east side?"

"We could cut one," said Solomon John.

"Yes, we could cut a door," exclaimed Agamemnon.

"But how can we tell whether there is any snow there?" asked Elizabeth Eliza, "for there is no window."

In fact, the east side of the Peterkins' house formed a blank wall. The owner had originally planned a little block of semidetached houses. He had completed only one, very semi and very detached.

"It is not necessary to see," said Agamemnon. "Of course, if the storm blows against this side of the house, the house itself must keep the snow from the other side."

"Yes," said Solomon John, "there must be a space clear of snow on the east side of the house, and if we could open a way to that"—

"We could open a way to the butcher," said Mr. Peterkin, promptly.

Agamemnon went for his pickax. He had kept one in the house for years but it was seldom used.

"What part of the wall had we better attack?" asked Mr. Peterkin.

Mrs. Peterkin was alarmed.

"What will Mr. Mudge, the owner of the house, think of it?" she exclaimed. "Have we a right to injure the wall of the house?"

"It is right to preserve ourselves from starving," said Mr. Peterkin. "The drowning man must snatch at a straw!"

"It is better that he should find his house chopped a little when the thaw comes," said Elizabeth Eliza, "than that he should find us lying about the house, dead of hunger, upon the floor."

Mrs. Peterkin was partially convinced.

The little boys came in to warm their hands. They had not succeeded in opening the side door, and were planning to try to open the door from the woodhouse to the garden.

"That would be of no use," said Mrs. Peterkin, "the butcher cannot get into the garden."

"But we might shovel off the snow," suggested one of the little boys, "and dig down to some of last year's onions."

Mr. Peterkin, Agamemnon, and Solomon John had been bringing together their carpenter's tools, and Elizabeth Eliza proposed using a gouge, if they would choose the right spot to begin.

The little boys were delighted with the plan, and hastened to find,—one, a little hatchet, and the other a gimlet. Even Amanda armed herself with a poker. "It would be better to begin on the ground floor," said Mr. Peterkin.

"Except that we may meet with a stone foundation," said Solomon John.

"If the wall is thinner upstairs," said Agamemnon, "it will do as well to cut a window as a door, and haul up anything the butcher may bring below in his cart."

Everybody began to pound a little on the wall to find a favorable place, and there was a great deal of noise. The little boys cut a bit out of the plastering with their hatchet and gimlet. Solomon John told Elizabeth Eliza that it made him think of stories of prisoners who cut themselves free, through stone walls, after days and days of secret labor.

Mrs. Peterkin, even, had come with a pair of tongs in her hand. She was interrupted by a voice behind her.

"Here's your leg of mutton, marm!"

It was the butcher. How had he got in?

"Excuse me, marm, for coming in at the side door, but the back gate is kinder blocked up. You were making such a pounding. I could not make anybody hear me knock at the side door."

"But how did you make a path to the door?" asked Mr. Peterkin. "You must have been working at it a long time. It must be near noon now."

"I'm about on regular time," answered the butcher. "The town team has cleared out the high road, and the wind has been down the last half hour. The storm is over."

True enough! The Peterkins had been so busy inside the house they had not noticed the ceasing of the storm outside.

"And we were all up an hour earlier than usual," said Mr. Peterkin, when the butcher left. He had not explained to the butcher why he had a pickax in his hand.

"If we had lain abed till the usual time," said Solomon John, "we should have been all right."

"For here is the milkman!" said Elizabeth Eliza, as a knock was now heard at the side door.

"It is a good thing to learn," said Mr. Peterkin, "not to get up any earlier than is necessary."

The Peterkins Buy a Cow

Not that they were fond of drinking milk, nor that they drank very much. But for that reason Mr. Peterkin thought it would be well to have a cow, to encourage the family to drink more, as he felt it would be so healthy.

Mrs. Peterkin recalled the troubles of the last cold winter, and how near they came to starving, when they were shut up in a severe snowstorm, and the water-pipes burst, and the milk was frozen. If the cow-shed could open out of the wood-shed such trouble might be prevented.

Tony Larkin was to come over and milk the cow every morning, and Agamemnon and Solomon John agreed to learn how to milk, in case Tony should be "snowed up," or have the whooping-cough in the course of the winter. The little boys thought they knew how already.

But if they were to have three or four pailfuls of milk every day it was important to know where to keep it.

"One way will be," said Mrs. Peterkin, "to use a great deal every day. We will make butter."

"That will be admirable," thought Mr. Peterkin.

"And custards," suggested Solomon John.

"And syllabub," said Elizabeth Eliza.

"I should think something might be done about covering her horns," said Mrs. Peterkin; "that seems the most dangerous part. Perhaps they might be padded with cotton."

Elizabeth Eliza said cows were built so large and clumsy that if they came at you they could not help knocking you over.

The little boys would prefer having the pasture a great way off. Half the fun of having a cow would be going up on the hills after her.

Agamemnon thought the feed was not so good on the hills.

"The cow would like it ever so much better," the little boys declared, "on account of the variety. If she did not like the rocks and the bushes she could walk around and find the grassy places."

"I am not sure," said Elizabeth Eliza, "but it would be less dangerous to keep the cow in the lot behind the house, because she would not be coming and going, morning and night, in that jerky way the Larkins' cows come home. They don't mind which gate they rush in at. I should hate to have our cow dash into our front yard just as I was coming home of an afternoon."

"That is true," said Mr. Peterkin; "we can have the door of the cow-house open directly into the pasture, and save the coming and going."

The little boys were quite disappointed. The cow would miss the exercise, and they would lose a great pleasure.

Solomon John suggested that they might sit on the fence and watch the cow.

It was decided to keep the cow in their own pasture; and, as they were to put on an end kitchen, it would be perfectly easy to build a dairy.

The cow proved a quiet one. She was a little excited when all the family stood around at the first milking, and watched her slowly walking into the shed.

Elizabeth Eliza had her scarlet sack dyed brown a fortnight before. It was the one she did her gardening in, and it might have infuriated the cow. And she kept out of the garden the first day or two, just to make sure.

Mrs. Peterkin and Elizabeth Eliza bought the best kind of milk-pans, of every size.

But there was a little disappointment about the taste of the milk.

The little boys liked it, and drank large mugs of it. Elizabeth Eliza said she could never learn to love milk warm from the cow, though she would like to do her best to patronize the cow.

Mrs. Peterkin was afraid Amanda did not understand about taking care of the milk; yet she had been down to overlook her, and she was sure the pans and the closet were all clean.

"Suppose we send a pitcher of cream over to the lady from Philadelphia to try," said Elizabeth Eliza."

"It might be awkward if she didn't like it"; said Solomon John. "Perhaps something is the matter with the grass."

"I gave the cow an apple to eat yesterday," said one of the little boys, remorsefully.

Elizabeth Eliza went over, and Mrs. Peterkin, too, and explained all to the lady from Philadelphia, asking her to taste the milk.

The lady from Philadelphia tasted, and said the truth was that the milk was sour.

"I was afraid it was so," said Mrs. Peterkin; "but I didn't know what to expect from these new kinds of cows."

The lady from Philadelphia asked where the milk was kept.

"In the new dairy," answered Elizabeth Eliza.

"Is that a cool place?" asked the lady from Philadelphia.

Elizabeth Eliza explained that it was close by the new kitchen.

"Is it near the chimney?" inquired the lady from Philadelphia.

"It is directly back of the chimney and the new kitchen range," replied Elizabeth Eliza. "I suppose it is too hot!"

"Well, well!" said Mrs. Peterkin, "that is it! Last winter the milk froze, and now we have gone to the other extreme! Where shall we put our dairy?"

—*Lucretia P. Hale.*

A Mix-Up Game

The Peterkins were always in trouble because they didn't think very well. Suppose that they also mixed up their words. Here are some sentences in which the words are in the wrong order. Write them in the right order on your paper.

"today will come nothing," said gloomily Agamemnon

"pig the there's!" Solomon suggested John

"we settle that need now not," Mr. said Peterkin

"we could open a butcher way the to," said Mr. promptly Peterkin

"that be admirable will," Mr. thought Peterkin

"cakes we milk the cocoa-nut for need don't," Mrs. said Peterkin

"the idea did not like I," Elizabeth said Eliza

"is cool a that place?" asked the Philadelphia from lady

Too Much Nature

PREPARATORY NOTE: One boy's hero was Robinson Crusoe. The other boy always talked of the adventures of Deerslayer. Read this story to learn what happened when the boys tried to imitate the outdoor life of their heroes.

The Boys Go Camping

"I think," said George, "that we ought to live on the country. Only tenderfeet take everything they need with them. With my trusty shotgun I can get all the meat we'll need. All we will need is some salt and a little flour. We can get milk from the cows and fish from the creek."

"We-e-ll," said Larry, who had been rather glad that Robinson Crusoe had a handy cargo of ship's goods to fall back on, "I don't know." Larry was rather fat, and fond of his food. He did not like very much the idea of living on the country.

"I sort of thought," he went on, "that it would be a good idea to take along five or six loaves of bread, some potatoes, a side of bacon and some ham."

"Pooh," said George, who was lively and thin. "That's not the way the Deerslayer did. With his trusty rifle, his powder horn and bullet bag, his knife and his flint and steel he went into the woods and lived for years. He wasn't any sissy."

"I'm no sissy, either," said Larry, "but I don't see any use of living on the country. Besides there isn't anything where we are going to live on. Except maybe a skunk or a woodchuck."

"Did you ever eat a woodchuck?" said George. "Why, there isn't anything better than a good old piece of roast woodchuck. My dad says they are as fat as a possum and just as good."

"We-e-ll," said Larry, "maybe. And anyhow we won't be far from home, so if we need to we can come back like Robinson Crusoe and get a few things."

The two boys were in the living room of Larry's home, a farmhouse two or three miles from where George lived. Larry and George went to the same school in the town and were in the same grade. George often came out to visit Larry and sometimes stayed all night.

School was out. The two boys faced a long summer in which there were many things to do, but the first of these was to go camping in the big woods which was about a mile away.

"I just love nature," said George, "I read about it all the time. And when I grow up I'm going to be a naturalist. They hunt birds and stuff 'em. Well, I've got to go home. I'll be out tomorrow with my stuff. You get ready and we'll get all set by tomorrow night and have our first camp."

"All right," said George. "I'll be ready. How you going to get out with your stuff?"

"Oh, my brother Frank'll bring me in the wagon he drives."

"Good," said Larry. "Be out early. It will take a good while to make our camp."

"O.K.," said George. He went out the door and trudged slowly in the hot June sunshine up the dusty clay road toward town.

The next morning George was up early and at the farm before Larry had finished taking the cows to pasture. Larry's sister, Sue, met him at the door.

"Here comes the great camper," said Sue. "Going to rough it in the wilds of the back pasture?"

"Yes," said George, "and I bet you'd be afraid to sleep for even part of a night that far from home."

Sue stuck her tongue out at George and he was saved from further insults by the arrival of Larry.

"I'm all ready," said Larry. "We'll take Jip and the light wagon. Got my stuff all in. Where's yours?"

George had a small heap of things by the gate where his brother Frank had left them. A roll of quilts, a lantern, an axe, a small box of food, a fish-pole, and a shotgun made up his equipment for the trail.

"Doesn't look like you got much to eat," observed Larry.

"I got plenty for me," said George, "just wait till you sink your teeth in that possum—woodchuck I'm going to roast."

George piled his things on the light wagon to which was hitched Larry's pony, Jip.

Larry's mother and Sue came to the door to watch them off.

"There go the Deerslayer and Robinson Crusoe," jeered Sue as the boys drove off.

"Hush up," said Larry's mother. "Be careful of the guns, boys, and be sure to put out your fire before you leave it."

"All right, Mother," called Larry. "Giddap, Jip."

Their road led up through the back pasture and over the hill out of sight. The Big Woods was at the far edge of the farm owned by Larry's father. Through it flowed a small river. And all around were other wooded pastures owned by neighbors. The boys were familiar with every part of the big woods, for they often had hunted squirrels and rabbits there.

Jip was a somewhat lazy pony, so their progress was slow. Jip stopped to rest often though the light wagon was not hard to pull. All Jip needed was a little encouragement and he would stand still all day. When Larry got impatient and hit him on his fat back with the lines, Jip looked around in an injured fashion. He walked faster for a step or two and then settled into a dragging walk.

At last they reached the Big Woods and the little river. They had already decided upon a camp site. Larry drove Jip under a big tree and stopped. Jip promptly went to sleep.

"Well," said George, "better get the tent up. Can't tell when it'll rain. Get our stores in under shelter and then we'll go hunting."

"Got to make the camp ship-shape first," said Larry. "There's a lot of things we got to do. Robinson Crusoe didn't do anything else for days but get fixed up in his cave."

"The Deerslayer could make camp in a minute," said George. "He didn't have a lot of truck to bother him. When he wanted to go to bed he just rolled up by the fire."

In the meantime, the two boys had been busy throwing things off the wagon. George's father had recently given him a tent. They put the poles together and prepared to set it up.

"They say," said George, "that you don't want to put your tent under a big tree, especially if it's the only tree around. Might get hit by lightning. Better get it where the sun will shine on it and keep it dry."

They selected a spot on the bank of the river and soon the tent was up. Then they began taking things inside.

"How we going to sleep?" asked Larry. "We forgot to bring along any cots."

"On the ground, of course," said George. "That's the way all real woodsmen sleep. I'll take this side and you take that." He threw his roll of quilts on one side.

"Well, all right," said Larry, "but I bet that ground will be hard. Wish I'd brought along a cot or two."

"Pooh," said George, "we aren't sissies. That ground'll be fine. It's got lots of nice soft grass on it."

"Now where'll we make our camp fire?" asked Larry. "It ought to be handy. How about here?"

"O.K.," said George. "Dig a place away in the sod and we won't catch the grass on fire. Let's get some rocks and put them around the fire to set things on.

Make a small fire like the Indians. The Indian said, 'White man heap big fool. Make big fire, roast himself. Indian make little fire. Keep cool!' "

"Yes," said Larry, "but we got to have a big enough fire to cook our food. Better make it plenty big." He dug in the tough sod with a shovel and threw the sod aside.

"All right," said George. "Now we're all fixed. Better get to hunting and get us some food. You all ready?"

"Yes, I guess so," said Larry, "but how about a little something before we go?"

"You're always thinking about eating," said George. "Can't eat now. You'll eat everything up the first day. The Deerslayer wasn't always eating."

"No, but Robinson Crusoe was always where there was plenty," said Larry. "He could get breadfruit right off the trees. How about one of those mock oranges there? Think it'd be any good?"

"Oh, stop talking about eating," said George.

George already had his small single-barreled shot-gun under his arm. Larry got slowly to his feet and hunted around in his bundles. He brought out a small rifle and the boys started off.

"You can't shoot squirrels and you can't shoot quail," said Larry. "They are protected now. You might get a young rabbit. Or maybe one of those groundhogs. Dad wants them killed anyhow. But I never heard of anyone eatin' a groundhog."

"They're the same as the woodchuck," said George. "I read they are very good. I'd like to try one."

The boys tramped along one bank of the river. Big oak, hickory, and other nut trees filled the glen where they were. Not far away a blue jay gave a harsh cry and as they went forward a crow rose out of the top of a big tree and cawed himself away.

"I'm the Deerslayer," said George, "and you're Rain-in-the-Face, my Indian companion. Keep your eye peeled for a deer."

"More likely to see a calf," said Larry, who some-times seemed to lack imagination.

Just then there was a crash in the brush behind them and George turned nervously and brought his gun to ready. A large shepherd dog bounded forward and gave every sign of being glad he was there with the two boys.

"Oh, there's Shep," said Larry. "I forgot him. Thought he might be good company. Meant to bring him along. Down, Shep."

"He'll be our trusty deerhound," said George. "Sic 'em, Shep."

They started forward and suddenly a rabbit jumped out from behind a stump and made away. Shep didn't wait for permission but went after the rabbit, barking at the top of his lungs.

"Aw, shoot," said George, "you couldn't hit the rabbit with that dog right in front of him."

Shep returned with his tongue hanging out, happy but with no rabbit. The boys tramped on. The Big Woods were still and they saw no game of any kind. After a while they turned back toward their camp. Just before they reached camp, they came to a fence. Several weathered boards that had once been a gate lay near the fence. Larry stopped and looked at them for a moment.

"I got an idea, George," he said. "We will make a bed out of those boards. You take my gun and I'll take one with us. Then we can come back after another. Might make us a table, too."

"Aw, the Deerslayer didn't have any bed or table," said George.

"Well, anyhow, I'm going to have one," said Larry, who was somewhat stubborn at times. He handed his rifle to George and shouldered one of the boards.

Soon they were back at their camp. Larry went back for more boards. George sat down and waited for him.

"Anyhow," he said, as Larry reappeared, "how are you going to saw 'em?"

"Saw 'em with a saw," answered Larry. "Brought one along. Thought it would come in handy."

"The Deerslayer didn't have any saw," said George.

"But I'm not the Deerslayer," said Larry.

"Beavers saw with their teeth," observed George.

"Yes, and a cricket makes noises with his hind legs, but that won't saw these boards," said Larry.

"Well, you don't need to get mad," said George.

George helped to get the remaining boards and with Larry doing most of the work, the boys proceeded to make a kind of bed. It was wonderful to behold. First Larry drove some sharpened stakes into the ground

in one corner of the tent. Then he dragged into camp some poles he found in the woods nearby.

"What are you going to do with those poles?" asked George.

"Going to make side and cross pieces to build the bed on."

"Seems to me you should use the fence boards for flat pieces; it would make the bed smoother."

"There's not enough boards for that. Just about enough to cover the frame," said Larry.

Larry had thoughtfully provided himself with some nails. Now he proceeded to place the fence boards crosswise of the frame, saw them off, and nail them down. The bed, when finished, presented the appearance of a corduroy road.

"Looks to me," said George, "as if that bed would be kinda hard."

"Better than sleeping on the ground," said Larry. "We'll pull some of that long grass to put on it. Then we'll put our quilts over that."

The boys found the grass rather hard to pull and soon became satisfied with a thin layer of grass on the rough boards. Then they covered it with quilts.

"Now," said Larry with a sigh, "there's a real bed for you."

Living On the Country

Just then they heard Shep barking in a wild, excited tone. They rushed out of the tent and over in the direction of the sound. Shep was after another rabbit.

"Let's see if we can get us a woodchuck," said George. "There's a lot of them over there on that side hill in the pasture. If we sneak up and keep out of sight, we can probably get one."

"All right," said Larry. So off they went toward the pasture, and on arriving there, were very careful not to be seen. They hid in some long grass and waited the arrival of Mr. Woodchuck. They had not long to wait. A fat woodchuck came out of a burrow and sat nibbling some grass.

"Get ready," whispered George. Both boys aimed. The rifle and the shotgun fired at the same time. Mr. Woodchuck dropped.

"Just like the Old Deerslayer," said George.

"Robinson Crusoe was a good shot, too."

Shep from somewhere far off heard the shots and came at top speed to find out what the excitement was about. He rushed for the woodchuck, but George beat him by a hair and held the animal up in triumph.

"He's nice and fat," said George. "Now for some good old roast woodchuck."

It took the boys a long time to skin Mr. Woodchuck and get him ready for the fire. By that time it was late afternoon and the sky was clouding.

"Looks a little like rain," said George, as they sawed away with a dull knife.

"We don't care," said Larry, "we got a good rainproof tent, haven't we?"

"I'll roast Mr. Woodchuck over the fire," said George. "You go down to the river and get some crawfish and we'll eat in style. They're just like lobster."

"Never heard of anyone eating crawfish," said Larry, "except a fish. How do you know they are any good?"

"Read about it in a book," said George.

That seemed to settle the matter, so Larry trudged down to the river while George drove two forked stakes in the ground by the fireplace and began to build a fire. He took a sharpened pole for a cross piece and ran it through Mr. Woodchuck. Soon the fire was blazing and George placed the spit across the forked uprights.

"Look-a-here, Larry," he said, when the fisherman returned, "this is the way to roast your venison. You turn it on the spit. That is the way they used to roast meat. Many's the time the Deerslayer roasted a haunch of venison just like I'm doing."

"Smell's kinda good," said Larry grudgingly. "Now what'll I do with these crawfish?"

"Put a can of water on the fire and let it boil," said George. "When it boils, drop the crawfish in."

"Don't you clean them?" inquired Larry.

"Naw," said George. "That's the way they cook lobsters. They don't need cleaning."

Larry settled down by the fire to let the water boil. "George," he said, "this is just about right. Here we are with the beauties of nature all around us. I'm feeling good."

"Me, too," said George. "Just smell old Mr. Woodchuck."

"Water's boiling," said Larry. He dropped the crayfish in the can. "Hey, George, they're turning red."

"Probably mad," said George.

Just then the boys became aware that something was happening all around them. While they had been busy at the fire, the clouds had risen steadily and the first large drops of rain began to fall. Wind was also blowing through the tops of the trees. Soon the rain began to fall in torrents. The fire died down and was soon out.

"Hurry up and get inside," said Larry. George took Mr. Woodchuck and beat a hasty retreat into the tent. Larry followed with the can of crayfish. The rain pelted down on the canvas.

"Too bad," said George. "But I'm sure this woodchuck is done. My, but I'm getting hungry. Guess we better have supper."

"Put some papers on the bed," he said, "and we'll soon have a feast. Cut some bread and sit down."

Larry spread out some papers and soon they were seated cross-legged on the bed ready to eat.

"Here yuh are," said George. He had sawed off a piece of woodchuck and handed it to Larry. Larry tried a bite.

A few minutes elapsed.

"George," said Larry, "this woodchuck seems kinda raw. And it's tough, too. I don't think much of your woodchuck."

"If the rain hadn't come," said George, "it would have been grand. There's nothing better than good roast woodchuck." He eyed the piece in his hand with disappointment. "Well, let's try the crayfish."

They fished the crayfish out of the can.

"Look's good," said George. He began working at the crayfish with a knife. But Larry took his in one bite. Silence for a few minutes.

"Say, George," said Larry, his mouth full of queer noises, "I think this would be good if it wasn't for the shells."

"Shells," said George. "You don't eat the shells. You take them off. There's some white meat inside, you know."

"Well, how was I to know?" asked Larry in a grieved tone. "You ought to tell a fellow about these new-fangled dishes of yours."

"Looks like," said George, after a few minutes silence, "we'd have to have a cold supper."

"Well," said Larry, "we've got some bread and butter and I got a side of bacon."

"You can't cook bacon now. The wood's all wet."

"Oh, that doesn't matter," said Larry. "Raw bacon's all right. We'll just saw off some and put it between the bread. That'll be better than nothing."

They chewed for a few minutes in silence on raw bacon sandwiches.

"These aren't so good," said George, "but anyhow, here we are snug as two bugs in a rug. And I like nature. There's nothing like nature. Just let me get out in the woods and I'm happy."

"Yes," said Larry. "I wonder what ma's having for supper."

"Many's the time the Deerslayer spent the night in the woods," said George, "with nothing to eat except some dried deer. You got to be tough to be a woodsman."

"Robinson Crusoe had a nice dry cave," said Larry. "He had plenty of ship's biscuit and everything. Don't know but what I'd rather be a sailor than a woodsman."

It was now growing dark. Larry lighted the kerosene lantern. It smoked a little and did not give much light. Just then Shep returned from an excursion in the woods and climbed up dripping on the bed.

"Hey, get out of here!" yelled Larry. "You'll have our nice bed all wet." Shep retreated shivering.

"Out there in front of the tent," said Larry after a while, "is Main Street. You're the chief of police. It's your duty to keep the cows out of Main Street. Think I hear one now."

"Aw, shucks!" said George, who for the moment was feeling somewhat more cheerful, "you be your own cow-catcher."

The rain had almost stopped. It was getting cool. Larry shivered. "Guess we better get to bed," he said. "Anyhow, we got a nice dry bed. Don't have to sleep on the ground." They crawled in under the quilts. For a time the sound of the rain on the tent seemed cozy.

"Say, Larry," said George after a while, "this bed feels kind of funny. I can feel every one of those ridges. It's as hard as the Rock of Gibraltar. Maybe more like the rocky road to Dublin."

The boys turned and tossed. Finally Larry got up. "I just thought of something. I forgot to set my throw line. I'm going to heave it out into the river and then tie the end to my toe. If a fish gets on in the night, I'll feel it and get up and catch him."

"That's a good idea," said George with enthusiasm. "A good fish for breakfast would taste fine. You go ahead and I'll stay here."

Larry groped around with the lantern among his things. He found the line and went outside. After a while he returned shivering. Removing his stocking, he tied the end of the line to his toe. Then to bed.

"Larry, you're as cold as ice," said George. "Stay over on your side."

The boys quieted down for a while. But as the night wore on, they tossed restlessly. George murmured in his sleep about rocky roads. Larry said something about Robinson Crusoe's hammock. The night wore on.

Suddenly outside there arose a clamor. Shep was busy again. A smell of a penetrating kind was wafted to them on the moist air.

George sat up. "Eh, pole cat," he said. "Pole cats are worth catching. Let's get up and see if Shep has got one. You can sell their skins."

"Did you ever catch a pole cat?" asked Larry.

"No," said George.

"Then you don't know any more about a pole cat than a Pole."

"What's a Pole?"

"I don't know. I think that they are folks that live up near the Pole."

"Eskimos aren't poles," said Larry. "They are just kinda polar. Polar. Get it, George, Haw! Haw!"

"I'm not dumb," said George.

"They live in the Polar circle," said Larry.

"Yes," said George, "and they hunt pole-cat bears. Get it, Larry? Pole-cat bears."

"What do you think I am?" asked Larry.

"Well," said George, "you're no pole-cat bear."

"Aw, cut it out," said Larry.

Silence for a while. The penetrating smell grew no less.

"Say, George," said Larry after some time had passed, "Do Eskimos wear arctics?"

"I don't know. Why?"

"Well, they live in the Arctic circle."

Silence again for what seemed hours.

"Say, Larry," said George finally, "that idea of yours about cots wasn't so bad. What say we get some tomorrow?"

"Oh, a great nature lover like you doesn't want any cot," murmured Larry. "We'll just sleep on the good old hard ground. It doesn't have any ruts in it."

"Ouch," Larry was out of bed, grabbing wildly at his foot. "Hey, George, come here and help me. Something's on my line. Ouch!"

George piled out of bed. Both boys were outside in the wet grass.

"It's one of those cows," said Larry, after struggling on the ground a few minutes. "She's running away with my line. Thought it was a whale."

Larry recovered his line and this time staked it on the bank of the river. The cold rain on the grass set the boys to shivering. They climbed back into bed and tossed and turned until a gray dawn finally wakened them.

"Guess we got too much nature," said Larry as he crawled out of the damp bed and got into his damper shoes. "No sense sleeping on a washboard and eating cold bacon. Drinking muddy water. Being waked up all times of the night."

"Aw, cheer up," said George. "We aren't sissies."

The boys had managed a breakfast of sorts after struggling for a long time to get a fire. After a while the sun came out. Things were more cheerful. They spent a morning prowling in the Big Woods.

As they returned to camp, they heard voices. "Yoo-hoo!" someone called.

"Gett'n' too crowded around here," said George.

Larry's mother, Sue and Larry's father were standing by the smouldering fire.

"Thought you boys might be lost," said Mr. Mills.

"How did you make out last night?" said Mrs. Mills. "You forgot your cots."

"What you got in that basket?" asked Larry hopefully.

"O some chicken, some boiled ham, potatoes, bread, and cookies."

"Gosh," said Larry. "We've had a little too much nature. Give me a piece of bread, some chicken, some ham, and a cooky, Ma. I'm glad my man Friday came on Tuesday. Gee, Ma."

"I thought," said Mrs. Mills, "that we'd have a picnic."

They were soon seated around a cloth under a tree.

"Don't give George much to eat, Ma," said Larry. "He doesn't like to eat."

"There's sense in all things," said George.

"Except in a skunk," said Larry. "His scent has no sense."

"Well, anyhow, we had adventures," said George.

"Isn't nature wonderful?" murmured Sue, grinning at the two boys.

"Aw, aw, you," said Larry.

—*Gerald Yoakam.*

Test and Study Exercises

1. Which two sentences best express the main thought of this story?

The boys camped by the river.

The boys found that "living on the country" was not so easy as they had expected.

The boys liked camping.

Sue laughed at Larry and George.

2. What did the boys have to eat on their trip?

3. How did the boys make a bed?

Suggested Activity

Find in some other book enough information about Robinson Crusoe and Deerslayer to tell you just who they were and some of the things they did. Be ready to tell the class a few of the facts you discover.

GLOSSARY

Key to Pronunciation

ā as in fāte   ē as in ēve   ī as in īce   ō as in ōld   ū as in ūse
ă as in făt   ĕ as in ĕnd   ĭ as in ĭll   ŏ as in ŏdd   ŭ as in ŭp
â as in câre   ē as in fērn   ĭ as in dĭrect   ô as in ôrb   û as in ûrn
à as in àsk   ê as in ĕvent   ŏ as in ŏbey   ū as in ūnite
ä as in ärm   ĕ as in enamĕl   oo as in boot   ŭ as in circŭs
å as in senåte   oͮo as in poͮor
à as in sofà   ŏ as in cŏnnect
ă as in ăccount

abated (à bāt′ĕd): stopped to some extent.

abed (à bĕd′): in bed.

Acropolis (à krŏp′ŏ lĭs): a hill in Athens.

adagio (à dä′jō): slow music.

adjust (ă jŭst′): change to fit, arrange.

ahoy (à hoi′): a shout to get attention.

allegro (ä lā′grō): fast music.

allegretto (ăl′ĕ grĕt′ō): lively music, not so fast as allegro.

alto (ăl′tō): voices lower than soprano.

Aphrodite (ăf′rŏ dī′tĕ): a Greek goddess.

Arapaho (à răp′à hō): name of an Indian tribe.

Aristotle (ăr′ĭs tŏt′′l): a great thinker in ancient Greece.

asunder (à sŭn′dĕr): apart, in two, in pieces.

Athena (à thē′nà): a goddess of the ancient Greeks.

attire (ă tīr′): clothing.

Bach (bäк): a great writer of music.

banyan (băn′yăn): a tree of which some of the roots grow from branches to the ground.

bracken (brăk′ĕn): common ferns.

bramble (brăm′b'l): rough shrubs with thorns.

breadfruit (brĕd′froot′): the fruit of a tree that grows in some South Sea Islands.

buckboard (bŭk′bōrd′): old-fashioned buggy drawn by horses.

bullock (boͮol′ŭk): an ox.

buoy (boo′ĭ): a marker that floats, used as a signal or a warning.

bypath (bī′pȧth′): a little side path.

bystanders (bī′stăn′dẽrs): people who look but take no part.

cantata (kăn tä′tȧ): music in the form of a play.

caress (kȧ rĕs′): a loving touch.

caste (kȧst): a class of people, in countries where there are different classes.

cherish (chĕr′ĭsh): love and care for.

Cherokee (chĕr′ȯ kē′): a tribe of Indians.

Chevalier (shĕv′ȧ lẽr′): title of honor.

Cheyenne (shī ĕn′): a tribe of Indians.

Chippewa (chĭp′ ĕwä): a tribe of Indians.

choral (kō′rȧl): music to be sung by groups.

clamor (klăm′ẽr): noise or excitement.

cleanliness (klĕn′lĭ nĕs): being clean.

cleft (klĕft): split.

coax (kōks): beg, urge.

colonel (kûr′nĕl): an army officer.

complicated (kŏm′plĭ kāt′ĕd): hard to do or make or understand.

confectioner (kŏn fĕk′shŭn ẽr): one who sells candy, ice cream, and other sweet things.

consequently (kŏn′sĕ kwĕnt-lĭ): as a result of something, or following something.

contradictory (kŏn′trȧ dĭk′tȯ-rĭ): not in agreement with something said or done.

Corot (kȯ′rō′): a French artist.

countryseats (kŭn′trĭ sēts′): country homes of wealthy people, also places of local government.

craftsmen (krȧfts′mĕn): people who work skillfully with their hands.

crest (krĕst): the top of something.

crevice (krĕv′ĭs): a crack, or a little valley.

crier (krī′ẽr): a man who used to shout, or cry, the news before there were newspapers

croon (kro͞on): sing softly.

crosswise (krŏs′wīz′): things placed or drawn across each other.

dachshund (däks′ho͞ont′): a small dog with a very long body and short legs.

dapple (dăp′′l): spotty.

defects (dė fĕkts′): faults, lack of good points.

defiance (dė fī′ăns): strong refusal to agree.

dell (dĕl): a little valley.

Demosthenes (dĕ mŏs′thĕ nēz): a great public speaker in ancient Greece.

disastrous (dĭ zȧs′trŭs): very bad, most unfortunate.

discourteous (dĭs kûr′tĕ ŭs): not polite.

dismount (dĭs mount′): get down, or get off.

drought (drout): a long time without rain.

duet (dū ĕt′): a musical performance by two people.

dumbfounded (dŭm′found′-ĕd): greatly surprised.

duration (dū rā′shŭn): during a certain time.

easel (ē′z′l): a frame which holds the canvas on which an artist paints.

elapsed (ĕ lăps′ĕd): passed, gone.

emphatic (ĕm făt′ĭk): forceful.

empress (ĕm′prĕs): wife of an emperor.

emu (ē′mū): a very large Australian bird.

enabled (ĕn ā′b′ld): made able.

encircling (ĕn sûr′k′l ĭng): surrounding, putting a circle around something.

exquisite (ĕks′kwĭ zĭt): very fine, delicate, lovely.

extravagant (ĕks trăv′a̤ gănt): wasteful, usually of money.

exult (ĕg zŭlt′): show great joy and happiness.

Falmouth (făl′mŭth): a town on the southern coast of England.

farthing (fär′thĭng): an English coin, worth about half a penny in our money.

feigned (fānd): pretended.

festivities (fĕs tĭv′ĭ tĭz): parties, jolly holiday celebrations.

finale (fĕ nä′lȧ): the end of something, usually the end of a musical piece.

fissure (fĭsh′ẽr): a narrow crack.

flounder (flound′ẽr): struggle, stumble.

foal (fōl): a colt.

forelegs (fōr′lĕgs′): the front legs of a four-legged animal.

fortnight (fôrt′nīt): two weeks.

fretful (frĕt′fo͝ol): annoyed, worried, disturbed.

gait (gāt): the manner of a person's or animal's walking or running, or the speed of their moving.

gentry (jĕn′trĭ): an old-fashioned word for people who have wealth, property, and education.

glossy (glŏs′ĭ): bright, shiny.

gouge (gouj): a kind of tool.

groom (grōōm): one who takes care of horses.

grudgingly (grŭj'ĭng lĭ): without pleasure.

headquarters (hĕd'kwâr'tērz): in the army the place where the highest officers do their work.

heather (hĕth'ēr): plants that grow on the heaths or waste lands of England and Scotland.

herb (ûrb): a plant used for flavors in cooking, and also in some medicines.

hewed (hūd): cut, usually with an ax.

hoist (hoist): lift, raise.

huzza (hŭ zä'): a cheer, or loud shout of pleasure.

indifferent (ĭn dĭf'ēr ĕnt): without interest in something; not caring.

infuriated (ĭn fū'rĭ āt ĕd): made very angry.

inquisitive (ĭn kwĭz'ĭ tĭv): curious, wanting to know.

intermezzo (ĭn'tēr mĕd'zō): a piece of music usually played between the acts of a longer work such as an opera or musical play.

interfere (ĭn'tēr fēr): to take part in someone else's business without being asked.

Iroquois (ĭr'ŏ kwoi): an Indian tribe.

Isle of Wight (īl ŏv wīt): a pretty island just south of England.

jangle (jăng'g'l): sounds that are not pleasant, either of voices in small arguments, or bells or other instruments not in tune.

jeer (jēr): a sound made with the voice to show that something is not liked.

knelt (nĕlt): down on the knees.

Lake Tahoe (lāk tä'hō): a mountain lake on the border between California and Nevada.

landlord (lănd'lôrd'): an owner of property which others rent or use.

landscape (lănd'skāp): all the land and what is on it that the eye can see at one time.

landwards (lănd'wērdz): toward land.

Le Havre (lẽ à'vr'): a French city on the sea coast.

legislator (lĕj'ĭs lā tẽr): a member of the group who make laws.

lender (lĕnd'ẽr): one who gives something with the hope of getting it back.

libretto (lĭ brĕt'ō): the words of a musical piece such as a song or an opera.

literally (lĭt'ẽr ăl lĭ): exactly.

livestock (līv'stŏk'): live farm animals.

maestro (mä ĕ'strȯ): a master or teacher, usually of music.

memorable (mĕm'ȯ rȧ b'l): worth remembering.

Millet (mē'lĕ'): a great French painter.

miniature (mĭn'ĭ ȧ tͧr): very small.

minuet (mĭn' û ĕt'): a delicate piece of music written for an old dance called the minuet.

Miserere (mĭz'ĕ rē'rĕ): a Latin word meaning *have mercy*, best known as a piece of music written to be sung with the words of a psalm from the Bible.

mistreated (mĭs trēt'ĕd): badly treated.

moderato (mŏd'ĕ rä'tō): moderate or medium time in music.

Mozart (mō'zärt): great Austrian writer of music.

naturalist (năt'ͧ rȧl ĭst): one who is a skilled student of nature.

Navajo (năv'ȧ hō): an Indian tribe.

neem (nēm): a tree of India having a sticky material sometimes used as medicine.

newcomer (nū'kŭm'ẽr): one who has not lived long in a certain place, or has not been long with a certain group.

notation (nȯ tā'shŭn): a note made to explain something or to keep the one who made it from forgetting.

nullah (nŭl'ȧ): a ravine, or little dry valley where water once flowed.

onlookers (ŏn'lŏŏk'ẽrs): those who look but take no part.

outwit (out wĭt'): to get an advantage over someone by quick thinking.

paddock (păd'ŭk): a small pasture, or a fenced space near buildings where horses are exercised.

palefaces (pāl'fās'ĕs): what the Indians called the white men.

parched (pärch'ĕd): dried, burned by dryness.

partially (pär'shăl lĭ): partly.

patronize (pā'trŭn īz): to give business to, or to help in other ways.

pedigree (pĕd'ĭ grē): the record of an animal's ancestors.

Pericles (pĕr'ĭ klēz): a great leader in ancient Greece.

perilous (pĕr'ĭ lŭs): dangerous.

Phidias (fĭd'ĭ ăs): a great sculptor in ancient Greece.

pianissimo (pē'ă nĭs'ĭ mō): most softly, a direction showing how music so marked should be played or sung.

Plato (plā'tō): a great thinker in ancient Greece.

poinsettia (poin sĕt'ĭ ȧ): a plant with rather large red leaves.

Port Said (pōrt sä ēd'): a port on the Mediterranean Sea, in Egypt.

preceding (prê sēd'ĭng): going before.

prescription (prē skrĭp'shŭn): directions for making something very carefully, such as medicine.

prow (prou): the front of something, usually of a boat.

prowling (proul'ĭng): walking quietly for a bad purpose.

rajah (rä'jȧ): a prince or chief in India.

reappeared (rē'ȧ pēr'ĕd): appeared again.

reassured (rē'ȧ shoor'ĕd): made free from fear or worry.

remorseful (rē môrs'fool): very sorry for something one has done.

resplendent (rē splĕn'dĕnt): bright and shining.

revered (rē vēr'ĕd): respected, believed in with respect.

rupee (roo pē'): a coin in India, worth about thirty-five cents in our money.

saber (sā'bĕr): sword.

scepter (sĕp'tēr): a special stick carried by a ruler as a sign of his position.

Schuylkill (shool'kĭl): a river in Pennsylvania.

scoff (skŏf): mock, laugh at in a mean way.

seawards (sē'wĕrds): toward the sea.

semicircle (sĕm'ĭ sûr'k'l): half circle.

sexton (sĕks'tŭn): one who rings the church bells and takes care of church property.

sheepish (shēp'ĭsh): a feeling one has after doing something silly that he is ashamed of.

sheik (shēk): a chief in Arabia.

shepherdess (shĕp'ĕrd ĕs): a woman shepherd.

shrewd (shrōōd): clever, not easily fooled.

Sioux (sōō): a tribe of Indians.

Sistine Chapel (sĭs'tēn chăp'ĕl): private chapel of the Pope, in Rome.

sleek (slēk): smooth.

solitary (sŏl'ĭ tĕr'ĭ): alone, single, one.

somber (sŏm'bēr): dark, sad, quiet.

spangles (spăng'g'ls): shiny ornaments.

spongy (spŭn'jĭ): like a sponge, soft and full of little holes.

stableman (stā'b'l măn): man who takes care of stables.

stalking (stôk'ĭng): walking proudly, strutting, but when used about hunters it means walking very quietly.

stifling (stī'flĭng): making it hard to breath because of heat or smoke.

stragglers (străg'lērs): those who have been lost from or have left a large group such as an army unit, and follow along behind.

stranded (strănd'ĕd): left on the shore.

stricken (strĭk'ĕn): hit by illness or other bad luck.

Suez (sōō ĕz'): a town on the Suez Canal at the north end of the Red Sea.

stylus (stī'lŭs): a sharp instrument for writing on wax.

tapering (tā'pēr ĭng): getting smaller at one end.

tempo (tĕm'pō): the time or rate of speed in playing or singing music.

Tioga Pass (tī ō'gȧ pȧs): a road crossing the Sierra Nevada Mountains near Yosemite National Park in California.

tradesman (trādz' măn): anyone who makes his living by buying and selling, usually one who has a store.

triple (trĭp''l): three times as much.

trustworthy (trŭst'wûr'thĭ): worthy of being trusted.

tumult (tū'mŭlt): noise and excitement.

turban (tûr'băn): hat formed by winding cloth around the head.

uneasy (ŭn ēz'ĭ): worried, afraid, not certain.

Ute (ūt): a tribe of Indians.

valor (văl′ẽr): bravery, courage.

veranda (vĕ răn′dȧ): porch.

veteran (vĕt′ẽr ȧn): one who has had experience, usually in war.

viola (vĕ ō′lȧ): a musical instrument with four strings, a little larger than a violin and of a lower pitch.

waistcoat (wās (t)′kōt′): a man's vest.

woodsmen (wo͝odz′mĕn): men who work in the woods.

Zeus (zūs): the chief god of the ancient Greeks.

zigzag (zĭg′zăg′): a line or path that changes directions very often.

DATE DUE

NOV 20 '65			
DEC 7 '65			
DEC 7 65			
DEC 15 '65			